INTERNATIONAL SERIES OF MONOGRAPHS ON

INORGANIC CHEMISTRY

GENERAL EDITORS: H. TAUBE AND A. G. MADDOCK

VOLUME 3

AN INTRODUCTION
TO CO-ORDINATION CHEMISTRY

A

AN INTRODUCTION TO
CO-ORDINATION
CHEMISTRY

by

D. P. GRADDON
M.Sc., Ph.D., F.R.I.C.

Senior Lecturer in Inorganic Chemistry
in the University of New South Wales

PERGAMON PRESS
NEW YORK · OXFORD · LONDON · PARIS
1961

PERGAMON PRESS INC.

122 East 55th Street, New York 22, N.Y.

Statler Center 640, 900 Wilshire Boulevard,
Los Angeles 17, California

PERGAMON PRESS LTD.

Headington Hill Hall, Oxford
4 & 5 Fitzroy Square, London, W.1

PERGAMON PRESS S.A.R.L.

24 Rue des Écoles, Paris V^e

PERGAMON PRESS G.m.b.H.

Kaiserstrasse 75, Frankfurt am Main

LIBRARY OF CONGRESS CARD NUMBER 60–16783

Set in Monotype Times 10 on 12 pt. and printed in Great Britain at
CHORLEY AND PICKERSGILL LTD LEEDS

PREFACE

PROGRESS in any science is seldom equally rapid all along the advancing front, but occurs rather in successive bursts at different points. Co-ordination chemistry has known two such periods of rapid advance. The first, occurring about the beginning of this century, was the period of classical co-ordination chemistry, when general principles were established and a solid foundation laid for later developments. At that time interest and controversy centred on Werner's theory, which stands today as one of the milestones in the progress of inorganic chemistry. But X-ray analysis has displaced the counting of isomers as a means of studying stereochemistry and whole new series of compounds have been obtained, of which even the prototypes were unknown fifty years ago. The new advance of co-ordination chemistry during the past two decades has been more, however, than a mere accumulation of new data. It has become apparent that the process of co-ordination, far from being an academic sideline, is one of the dominant factors determining the chemistry of the elements.

In this book I have tried to present a brief account of some aspects of this new advance. It is therefore arranged as a series of discussions on related themes rather than as a description of the co-ordination compounds of individual elements. I am conscious that some important topics are omitted, in particular the relationship between colour and constitution in the transition metal complexes, the problem of reaction mechanisms, and the function of co-ordination in natural products; all of these topics have been omitted for the same reason — it did not seem to me that, on the experimental evidence now available, it was yet possible to provide a reasonably complete account.

As this book is intended primarily for students, I have, wherever possible, given references to review articles rather than original publications; but this is not always possible, and in referring to original publications I have usually referred to the most recent, irrespective of its importance, as this will provide a lead into the particular topic. References are also given to original publications of X-ray analyses, as their date is so important a guide to reliability. As so much of the work described in Chapters I and VII is so very well known, there are no references in these chapters, but such references are available in larger works quoted in the bibliography.

My grateful thanks are due to Mr. L. Munday, senior lecturer in organic chemistry at Birkenhead Technical College, England, for reading the manuscript and offering many helpful suggestions.

D.P.G.

Sydney, June 1960

CONTENTS

CHAPTER I

HISTORICAL INTRODUCTION

HISTORICALLY co-ordination chemistry is of comparatively recent origin. Co-ordination compounds were unknown to the Arabian chemists of the Middle Ages and the Alchemists did not come upon them. The earliest recorded co-ordination compound is probably prussian blue, obtained by the artists' colour maker, Diesbach, in Berlin during the first decade of the eighteenth century. Its discovery, like so many important developments in the history of chemistry, was accidental, the blue pigment being obtained as a by-product when animal refuse and soda were heated in an iron pot. Iron, indeed, seems to have played an important part in the accidental advancement of co-ordination chemistry as it was involved in the discovery of three other types of co-ordination compound: the carbonyls in 1891, the phthalo-cyanins in 1926 and the *cyclo*pentadienyls in 1951.

In 1753 Macquer by treating prussian blue with alkali obtained "yellow prussiate of potash" (potassium ferrocyanide), from which Scheele 30 years later isolated prussic acid, describing among other properties its smell and taste and surviving, miraculously, to report his results. Another early example of the use of co-ordination compounds, dating from about 1760, was Lewis's method of refining platinum through the sparingly-soluble potassium chloroplatinate.

The beginning of co-ordination chemistry, however, is usually dated from the discovery of the cobaltammines by Tassaert in 1798. Tassaert observed that ammoniacal solutions of cobalt chloride deposited the orange compound $CoCl_3.6NH_3$ on standing overnight, and recognized in this a new type of chemical substance, formed by the combination of two already fully-saturated compounds, but possessing properties quite different from either.

During the following half century increasing numbers of these "complex" compounds were obtained, not only of cobalt but also of other elements, for instance "red prussiate of potash" (potassium ferricyanide) in 1822, Magnus's green salt in 1828 and the nitroprussides in 1849. The large numbers of cobaltammines known necessitated a system of naming and, as their structures were not understood, Fenny, in 1851–1852, introduced the familiar colour-code nomenclature, a few typical examples of which are shown overleaf.

At this time several theories were proposed to explain the nature of these "complex" compounds. One of the most favoured was that of Graham in

1

1837, suggesting that the compounds were ammonium salts in which one of the hydrogen atoms was replaced by a metal atom; though at that time not very helpful to the further understanding of these compounds, this idea has a remarkable affinity with the modern Lewis-acid–base approach to the process of co-ordination.

COLOUR-CODE NOMENCLATURE

Formula	Colour	Colour-code name
$CoCl_3.6NH_3$	yellow	luteocobaltic chloride
$CoCl_3.5NH_3$	purple	purpureocobaltic chloride
$CoCl_3.5NH_3.OH_2$	red	roseocobaltic chloride
$CoCl_2.(NO_2).5NH_3$	brown	xanthocobaltic chloride
$CoCl_3.4NH_3$	green	praseocobaltic chloride

In 1854 Claus, on the basis of studies of the platinum ammines, put forward a view not unlike that of Werner 40 years later: he recognized the submergence of the usual properties of the ammonia and the metal in the complex salts, but that the equivalence of the metal was unaffected; he also drew the parallel between the complex salts and the salt hydrates. Claus's ideas, however, were not generally accepted and in 1858 an event occurred which was to hold back the development of inorganic chemistry for nearly half a century. This was Kekulé's demonstration of the tetravalency of carbon and the chain structure of the higher hydrocarbons, and the mental climate of chain structures which followed. Within 10 years Blomstrand had produced his famous chain theory of the structure of complex ammines, the complexes $PtCl_2.4NH_3$ and $CoCl_2.6NH_3$, for example, being represented:

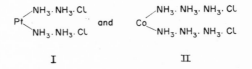

I   II

Formulae of this sort could be arranged so as to account for the accumulating evidence of abnormalities in the behaviour of some of the non-metal atoms in the complex salts, such as the precipitation by silver nitrate of only two-thirds of the chlorine in purpureocobaltic chloride: this was explained by Jorgensen* on the assumption that the instantly-reactive

---

* At this time the cobaltammines were all supposed to be dimeric, e.g. $Co_2Cl_6.12NH_3$, and all Blomstrand's formulae were doubled. The monomeric structures were established by Jorgensen in 1890, but there seems to be no purpose served by doubling these early formulae in the text.

chlorine atoms were situated at the ends of $(NH_3)_n$ chains, but the unreactive atom was attached directly to the cobalt atom (III):

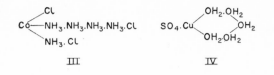

III   IV

The unfortunate influence of the contemporary development of organic chemistry is again seen in Wurtz's cyclic structures for the salt hydrates (IV), proposed in 1879. In 1887, however, Arrhenius introduced the conception of ionization and within only a few years inorganic chemistry began to develop again along its rightful course.

WERNER'S THEORY

In 1891 Werner published the first of his papers on complex compounds, in which he suggested that an atom does not necessarily have a fixed small number of valence bonds, but that its valency might be exerted over the whole surface of the atom and be divided into various units of different strength. This he developed 2 years later into the well-known concept of "primary" and "secondary" valencies, which has remained the basis of co-ordination chemistry ever since.

According to Werner the "primary" valencies were those involved in satisfying the chemical equivalence of the atom and the "secondary" valencies were those by which the "co-ordinated" molecules of ammonia were attached, so that in luteocobaltic chloride, for example, the three primary valencies of the cobalt are used to attach the three chlorine atoms and six secondary valencies are required to retain the six co-ordinated ammonia molecules. In the roseo salt, $CoCl_3.5NH_3.OH_2$, one of the six secondary valencies binds the water molecule. When this salt is heated it loses water, giving the purpureo salt, $CoCl_3.5NH_3$; Werner's explanation of the precipitation of only two thirds of the chlorine in this compound by silver nitrate is that one of the chlorine atoms has become attached by a secondary valency, replacing the lost water molecule. It thus appears that although the primary valencies may not all be used, the secondary valencies invariably are. Loss of another molecule of ammonia as in the praseo salts, $CoCl_3.4NH_3$, thus leads to only one-third of the chlorine being precipitated by silver nitrate. One of the consequences of Werner's theory (and a test point, since it predicts here a different result from the chain theories) is that the loss of yet another molecule of ammonia from the praseo salt should give a compound $CoCl_3.3NH_3$, from which silver nitrate should not precipitate any of the chlorine. Unfortunately no such compound can be prepared.

From the above evidence it is apparent that one of the differences between primary and secondary valencies is that the primary allow ionization of the bound atoms whereas the latter do not. Although the crucial compound $CoCl_3.3NH_3$ could not be made, several series of compounds are known in which three or more molecules of ammonia are replaced by other groups, for example the complete series:

$Co(NO_2)_3.6NH_3$ $PtCl_4.6NH_3$

$Co(NO_2)_3.5NH_3$ $PtCl_4.5NH_3$

$Co(NO_2)_3.4NH_3$ $PtCl_4.4NH_3$

$Co(NO_2)_3.3NH_3$ $PtCl_4.3NH_3$

$Co(NO_2)_3.2NH_3.KNO_2$ $PtCl_4.2NH_3$

$Co(NO_2)_3.NH_3.2KNO_2$ $PtCl_4.NH_3.KCl$

$Co(NO_2)_3.3KNO_2$ $PtCl_4.2KCl$

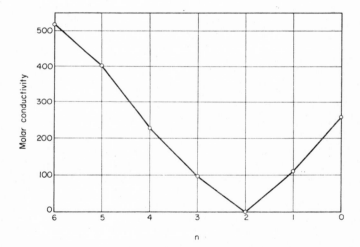

FIG. 1.   Molar conductivities of the platinum-IV complexes $Pt(NH_3)_nCl_{6-n}$ and $K_{2-n}Pt(NH_3)_nCl_{6-n}$, showing $[Pt(NH_3)_2Cl_4]$ as a non-electrolyte

Werner investigated many of these series by the conductivity method and showed that successive loss of ammonia molecules resulted in the formation of successively fewer ions, the compounds $Co(NO_2)_3.3NH_3$ and $PtCl_4.2NH_3$, for example, being non-electrolytes (Fig. 1).

In this way the precipitation by silver nitrate of two-thirds and one-third of the chlorine in $CoCl_3.5NH_3$ and $CoCl_3.4NH_3$ was shown to correspond with the formation of three and two ions in solution, so that the formulae become:

$$[Co(NH_3)_5Cl]^{2+} \, 2Cl^-$$
$$[Co(NH_3)_4Cl_2]^+ \, Cl^-$$

the secondary valencies remaining in full use.

ISOMERISM

One feature of the chemistry of complex compounds more characteristic of organic chemistry than inorganic is the formation of isomers. Thus, roseocobaltic bromide (V), like the chloride, loses water on heating and forms a bromopurpureo salt (VI), which reacts with silver sulphate to give the violet sulphate (VII):

$$[Co(NH_3)_5(OH_2)]Br_3 \rightarrow [Co(NH_3)_5Br]Br_2 \rightarrow [Co(NH_3)_5Br](SO_4)$$
$$\text{(V)} \qquad\qquad \text{(VI)} \qquad\qquad \text{(VII)}$$

By the action of concentrated sulphuric acid on the chloropurpureo compound (VIII) a sulphatopurpureo bisulphate (IX) is formed, from which can be obtained the corresponding bromide (X). Both (IX) and (X) are binary electrolytes:

$$[Co(NH_3)_5Cl]Cl_2 \rightarrow [Co(NH_3)_5(SO_4)](SO_4H) \rightarrow [Co(NH_3)_5(SO_4)]Br$$
$$\text{(VIII)} \qquad\qquad \text{(IX)} \qquad\qquad \text{(X)}$$

The compounds (VII) and (X) are isomeric, but can be readily distinguished by their reactions with silver and barium salts. Another example of this type of isomerism, known as "ionization isomerism", is provided by the compounds $[Pt(NH_3)_4Cl_2]Br_2$ and $[Pt(NH_3)_4Br_2]Cl_2$.

A special case of this type of isomerism occurs when one of the groups involved is a solvent molecule; in this case it is referred to as "solvate isomerism" or, if water is the solvent, "hydrate isomerism". An example is the series of compounds of the formula $CrCl_3.6H_2O$: crystallization of acid aqueous solutions of chromic chloride gives a dark green compound $CrCl_3.6H_2O$, from which silver nitrate precipitates one-third of the chlorine and desiccation over sulphuric acid removes two molecules of water. A light green form of the hexahydrate is obtained by passing gaseous hydrogen chloride into an ethereal solution of chromic chlorosulphate, $CrClSO_4$, and loses only one molecule of water on desiccation, two-thirds of the chlorine being precipitated by silver nitrate. By precipitation of an aqueous solution of chrome alum with gaseous hydrogen chloride a violet form is obtained, which loses no water on desiccation and from which silver nitrate precipitates the whole of the chlorine immediately. Clearly the three forms can be represented by the formulae:

violet form	$[Cr(OH_2)_6]Cl_3$
light green form	$[Cr(OH_2)_5Cl]Cl_2.H_2O$
dark green form	$[Cr(OH_2)_4Cl_2]Cl.2H_2O$

In solution an equilibrium is set up, the proportions of the various isomers depending on the temperature and concentration, very dilute solutions containing almost exclusively the violet form.

"Co-ordinate isomerism" is another form of isomerism attributable to interchange of the metal atoms in two compounds, as exemplified by the two compounds $[Co(NH_3)_6][Cr(CN)_6]$ and $[Cr(NH_3)_6][Co(CN)_6]$. Another type of isomerism which can occur is that known as "polymerization isomerism"; an example in the cobalt series is the isomerism of the non-electrolyte $[Co(NH_3)_3(NO_2)_3]$ with hexammine cobaltic cobaltinitrite, $[Co(NH_3)_6][Co(NO_2)_6]$, which has double the formula. The most familiar example of this type of isomerism occurs, however, in the complexes of divalent platinum: at low temperatures the action of ammonia on potassium chloroplatinite, $K_2[PtCl_4]$, gives "Magnus's green salt", formulated $[Pt(NH_3)_4][PtCl_4]$, since silver nitrate reacts with it to give $Ag_2[PtCl_4]$. On heating, Magnus's green salt gives a yellow non-electrolyte, $[Pt(NH_3)_2Cl_2]$, which is of course an isomer.

One other simple type of isomerism occurs in these compounds. This is "structural isomerism", which depends upon the possibility of one of the co-ordinated groups being linked to the central atom by different atoms. An example is the two compounds $[Co(NH_3)_5(NO_2)]Cl_2$. A red form of this compound is obtained by the action of dilute nitrous acid on purpureo-cobaltic chloride; it is unstable to acids, which convert it to a brown form, the well-known xantho salt:

$$[Co(NH_3)_5Cl]Cl_2 \rightarrow [Co(NH_3)_5(ONO)](NO_2)_2 \rightarrow [Co(NH_3)_5(ONO)]Cl_2$$
$$\downarrow$$
$$[Co(NH_3)_5(NO_2)](NO_2)_2 \rightarrow [Co(NH_3)_5(NO_2)]Cl_2$$

The xantho salts are also obtained by the direct action of nitrous fumes on ammoniacal solutions of cobalt salts; in them the NO_2^- group inside the complex is attached to the cobalt through the nitrogen atom, whereas in the unstable red forms it is attached through an oxygen atom:

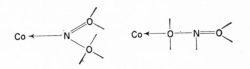

STEREOCHEMISTRY OF 6:CO-ORDINATED COMPOUNDS

The presence in a complex compound of six groups attached by secondary valencies to the metal atom raises a similar stereochemical problem to that posed to the organic chemists by the molecule of benzene. As in this earlier example there are three reasonable structures to choose from: the flat hexagon (XI), the trigonal prism (XII), and the octahedron (XIII), each with the metal atom in the middle. As in the case of benzene, the choice was made on the basis of the number of stereoisomers obtainable with molecules or ions of the form MA_nB_{6-n}.

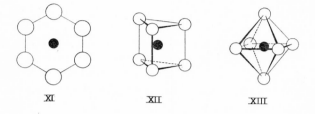

XI   XII   XIII

The most important compounds affecting the distinction between the stereochemical possibilities were those of the type MA_4B_2, which should exist in three isomeric forms if hexagonal or trigonal prismatic, but only two if octahedral, the *cis* (XIV) and *trans* (XV):

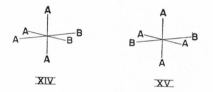

XIV   XV

Numerous compounds of this type are now known in two isomeric forms, but none in more than two, indicating the octahedral structure, later confirmed by much other evidence, including numerous X-ray analyses.

In most cases the *cis*-isomers are less stable than the *trans*-isomers, but they can sometimes be obtained by the displacement of a bidentate group (i.e. a group such as ethylenediamine which can co-ordinate twice to the same metal atom and must occupy two adjacent co-ordination positions). One of the testing points of Werner's theory concerned the existence of a second isomer of praseocobaltic chloride, $[Co(NH_3)_4Cl_2]Cl$; at the time only the green (*trans*) isomer was known and all attempts to obtain another had failed. The second isomer, predicted by the theory, was eventually made by Werner by a series of reactions, the last of which involved replacement of a bidentate group by the two chlorine atoms (shown on page 8).

It may be noted that in this example the bidentate group is in fact a double bridge formed by the co-ordination of the hydroxyl ions to two cobalt atoms at the same time. Many such bridged polynuclear complex salts are known.

The presence of three bifunctional groups in a complex leads to the possibility of optical isomerism. Such isomers, represented by the diagrams

(XVI) and (XVII), were predicted by Werner and numerous examples were subsequently resolved by him, including the ions $[Co(en)_3]^{3+}$, $[Cr(en)_3]^{3+}$, $[Rh(en)_3]^{3+}$, $[Ir(en)_3]^{3+}$, $[Rh(C_2O_4)_3]^{3-}$ and $[Fe(dipy)_3]^{3+}$ (the abbreviations "en" and "dipy" represent ethylenediamine and 2:2´-dipyridyl, respectively).

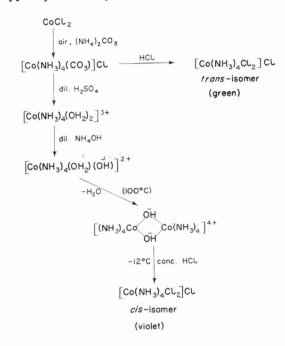

$$CoCl_2$$

air, $(NH_4)_2CO_3$

$$[Co(NH_3)_4(CO_3)]Cl \xrightarrow{\text{HCl}} [Co(NH_3)_4Cl_2]Cl$$

trans-isomer
(green)

dil. H_2SO_4

$$[Co(NH_3)_4(OH_2)_2]^{3+}$$

dil. NH_4OH

$$[Co(NH_3)_4(OH_2)(OH)]^{2+}$$

$-H_2O$ (100°C)

$$\left[(NH_3)_4Co\begin{array}{c}OH\\ \diagdown\\OH\end{array}Co(NH_3)_4\right]^{4+}$$

$-12°C$ | conc. HCl

$$[Co(NH_3)_4Cl_2]Cl$$

cis-isomer
(violet)

When two bidentate groups and two single ligands are attached to the metal atom, combinations of optical and *cis/trans*-isomerism are possible, leading to three isomers: a *trans*-form (XVIII) with planes of symmetry and two optical isomers of the *cis*-form (XIX, XX).

XVI   XVII

The combination of these fundamental forms of stereoisomerism with one another and with the introduction of asymmetric organic molecules as ligands (e.g. propylenediamine), together with the possibilities of internal compensation (*meso*-forms) in polynuclear complexes leads to innumerable permutations which have been explored in much detail. While no purpose would be served by reproducing here a detailed account of these experiments, it is, perhaps, worth noting that in Werner's time optical activity was considered to be a phenomenon of organic chemistry and there were still many

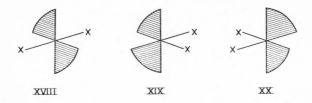

XVIII   XIX   XX

who considered the optical activity of these complex compounds to be in some way due to the organic part of the molecule. Werner therefore prepared and resolved into optical isomers a wholly inorganic compound, containing the tetranuclear complex ion $[Co\{<\frac{OH}{OH}>Co(NH_3)_4\}_3]^{6+}$, obtained by the action of ammonia on the salts of the ion $[Co(NH_3)_4(OH_2)Cl]^{2+}$.

STEREOCHEMISTRY OF 4:CO-ORDINATED COMPLEXES

The formation of a yellow non-electrolyte, $[Pt(NH_3)_2Cl_2]$, from Magnus's green salt has been mentioned in connexion with polymerization isomerism. This compound reacts with ammonia to form the tetrammine salt, $[Pt(NH_3)_4]Cl_2$, which when boiled with hydrochloric acid gives a non-electrolyte, $[Pt(NH_3)_2Cl_2]$, isomeric with the above compound, but differing from it in physical properties. These two isomers known, respectively, as the α- and β-diammine platinous chlorides, led Werner to the conclusion that the platinum atom, unlike the atoms commonly present in organic compounds, had square-planar stereochemistry.

On chemical grounds the β-isomer is assigned the *trans*-structure (XXI) and the α-isomer the *cis*-structure (XXII). The chemical evidence is considerable and complicated and only two examples of the numerous experiments on which the conclusions are based will be quoted, both based on the necessary *cis*-configuration of bidentate ligands:

(1) Both isomers react with moist silver oxide to give bases of the form $[Pt(NH_3)_2(OH)_2]$; oxalic acid displaces the hydroxyl groups and the α-isomer gives a non-electrolyte (XXIII), whereas the β-isomer gives a dibasic acid (XXIV) as the oxalate ion is unable to act as a bidentate group.

(2) The α-isomer reacts with ethylenediamine to form a tetrammine (XXV). An identical tetrammine is formed by the action of ammonia on the non-electrolyte obtained from ethylenediamine and potassium chloroplatinite.

The square-planar structure and the allocation of configurations to the two isomers has been confirmed subsequently by X-ray analysis and by measurement of dipole moments. This last is a widely-used method of physical determination of absolute configuration; perfectly-symmetrical complexes of the *trans*-type, such as $[(R_3P)_2PtX_2]$, have zero dipole moments since the moments of individual bonds cancel one another; *cis*-isomers on

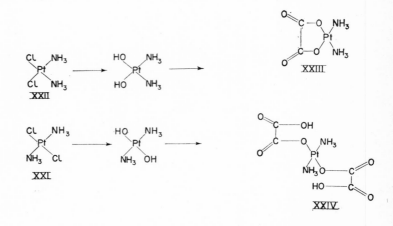

the other hand have a resultant moment. One limitation of this method arises where the ligands do not have an axis of symmetry along the metal–ligand linkage (for example primary amines); although the moments of the metal–ligand bonds will cancel in the *trans*-isomers of such compounds, there may be resultant moments across the plane of the molecule due to the asymmetry of the ligands themselves, but such moments are usually comparatively small.

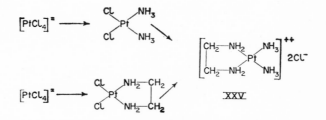

As with the 6:co-ordinated complexes the classical confirmation of the square-planar structure of platinous complexes was by isomer counts, in particular by the isolation of all three isomers of compounds of the type [PtABCD]; the alternative tetrahedral structure would give only two (optical) isomers. The first complete set of three isomers to be obtained was of the compound [Pt(NH₃)(NO₂)(NH₂OH)(pyridine)] the three isomers being obtained by the reactions shown below.

Though the square-planar configuration is fully established for the 4:co-ordinated complexes of divalent platinum, this stereochemical arrangement is not common with the compounds of other elements. As might be expected the 4:co-ordinated complexes of divalent palladium resemble those of platinum very closely and their square-planar structure is also well established.

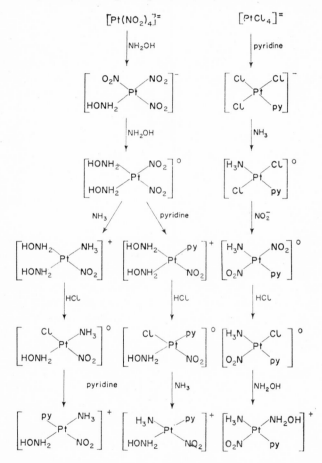

Many compounds of divalent nickel are also planar, though there is a strong tendency for these to form octahedral complexes by further co-ordination and a few of the 4:co-ordinated complexes are tetrahedral; a similar relationship between square-planar and octahedral co-ordination occurs in the complexes of divalent copper; the stereochemistry of these two elements is discussed in detail in Chapter II. The only other ion which almost invariably has square-planar co-ordination is that of trivalent gold, the Au^{3+} and Pt^{2+} ions being isoelectronic; the chemistry of 4:co-ordinated auric compounds is discussed in Chapter III.

All other 4:co-ordinated elements appear to form tetrahedral complexes, some typical examples being the complex ions: $[BeF_4]^{2-}$, $[BF_4]^-$, $[AlCl_4]^-$, $[GaCl_4]^-$, $[CoCl_4]^{2-}$, $[Zn(CN)_4]^{2-}$, $[HgI_4]^{2-}$. In the case of the complexes of divalent cobalt, however, there is still some doubt whether some of the 4:co-ordinated complexes may be square-planar; these complexes frequently exist in two differently-coloured isomers and this isomerism has been attributed to differences in configuration, one isomer being tetrahedral and one planar; these complexes are all of much lower stability than the platinous complexes so that the traditional methods of structure determination by counting isomers, etc., cannot be applied and the solution of this problem will depend upon the complete X-ray analysis of large numbers of these complexes.

CHAPTER II

MODERN THEORIES OF CO-ORDINATION CHEMISTRY

THE OCTET THEORY — EFFECTIVE ATOMIC NUMBER

WERNER'S theory was a landmark in the development of "complex" chemistry. It made it possible to understand the existence of hundreds of complex compounds, explained their stereochemistry, and made many predictions, particularly about their isomerism, which were subsequently confirmed experimentally. It remains the foundation on which any account of co-ordination compounds must be based. It could not, however, explain why certain elements had this remarkable ability to form numerous complex compounds, since the theory antedated by two decades the elucidation of the electronic structure of the atom, upon which all modern theoretical chemistry is founded.

We can now appreciate that the difference between Werner's primary and secondary valencies is the difference between ionic and covalent bonds. Thus, if we consider the typical series of ammines $[Co(NH_3)_4Cl_2]Cl$, $[Co(NH_3)_5Cl]Cl_2$ and $[Co(NH_3)_6]Cl_3$, the precipitation by silver nitrate of one, two and three atoms of chlorine, respectively, appears as evidence of the ionic binding of the corresponding number of chlorine atoms. The other chlorine atoms can be precipitated by silver nitrate after the prolonged action of alkali, a similar reaction to that required to cleave the carbon–halogen bonds in the alkyl halides.

The Co-ordinate Bond

To earlier generations one of the puzzling features of "complex" chemistry was the formation of chemical bonds between ions and complete molecules such as ammonia. This is readily explained by the electronic theory of atomic structure. In an ammonia molecule the nitrogen atom has a complete octet of electrons, six shared with the three hydrogen atoms to form covalent bonds, two unshared. In some other molecules, for instance boron fluoride, one of the atoms has two electrons less than are required to complete the octet. When molecules of ammonia react with molecules of boron fluoride

13

the octet on the boron atom is completed by co-ordination of the unshared pair of electrons on the ammonia molecule:

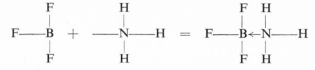

The B—N bond so produced is a covalent bond, differing from an ordinary covalent bond in that both bonding electrons came originally from the same atom. This atom is referred to as the "donor" atom and the boron atom is the "acceptor" atom. Any molecule or ion having unshared pairs of electrons can act as a donor molecule and any ion or atom having an electronic structure which can be made up to an inert gas structure, or other stable electronic configuration, can act as an acceptor. The best-known examples of each type are:

Donors: neutral molecules of elements in groups VB, VIB and VIIB, e.g. NH_3, NR_3, OH_2, OR_2, SR_2, PF_3; anions of elements in groups VB, VIB, VIIB, e.g. NH_2^-, OH^-, F^-, Cl^-, Br^-, I^-; various other simple molecules or ions such as CO, CN^-.

Acceptors: neutral molecules of elements in group III, e.g. BF_3, $AlCl_3$, $B(CH_3)_3$; ions of the transition metals, e.g. Cr^{3+}, Fe^{2+}, Pt^{4+}, Cu^{2+}; H^+.

Co-ordination Number

Molecules such as boron fluoride or aluminium chloride can accept only one pair of electrons, but ions of the transition metals require larger numbers of electrons to bring their electronic structures up to that of the next inert gas and so can accommodate several donor groups (ligands). The number of ligands accommodated is known as the co-ordination number. The electronic structure of the metal atom in the complex then corresponds to that of another element; it is said to have the "effective atomic number" of this other element.

In the B sub-groups of the periodic table the ions of elements in their group valency state all require eight electrons to reach the effective atomic number of the next inert gas; the expected co-ordination number of four is observed in many complex salts, for example the neutral molecule $ZnCl_2(NH_3)_2$ and the ions $Cu(CN)_4^{3-}$, $GaCl_4^-$, HgI_4^{2-}. The same co-ordination number is shown by the Cu^{2+}, Ni^{2+} and Co^{2+} ions (with vacancies for nine, ten and eleven electrons, respectively), but the Fe^{2+} ion, and the similar Co^{3+} and Pt^{4+} ions, which can accommodate twelve electrons, form complexes with co-ordination number six, as do most of the transition metal ions with vacancies for more than twelve electrons. The Mo^{4+} and W^{4+} ions, with vacancies for sixteen electrons, however, do form 8:co-ordinated complex cyanides, $Mo(CN)_8^{4-}$ and $W(CN)_8^{4-}$.

In the first and second long periods ions of inert-gas structure require eighteen electrons to complete the next inert-gas structure. The large co-ordination number of nine is probably impossible for geometrical reasons and in the first long period these ions are usually 6:co-ordinate (as in TiF_6^{2-}); the larger ions in the second and third long periods sometimes have higher co-ordination numbers, e.g. ZrF_7^{3-}, TaF_8^{3-}.

Limitations of the Octet Theory

Whereas this simple electronic approach accounts for the co-ordination numbers of most of the common complex forming ions, it leaves unexplained the directive nature of the bonds; unless indeed this is regarded as a natural geometrical result of the mutual repulsion of the ligands. The peculiar, square-planar co-ordination observed in the complexes of the divalent ions of nickel, palladium, platinum and copper and of trivalent gold cannot, however, be explained geometrically; nor can the failure of the Ni^{2+}, Pd^{2+} and Pt^{2+} ions to form 5:co-ordinated complexes.

In addition to the 4:co-ordinated complexes, divalent nickel also forms a number of complexes with the co-ordination number six, for example the ammine $[Ni(NH_3)_6]^{2+}$. In these the number of donated electrons to be accommodated necessitates exceeding the next inert-gas structure on the nickel atom. The inert-gas structure is also exceeded in many 6:co-ordinated complexes of B sub-group elements, such as the ammines $[Zn(NH_3)_6]^{2+}$ and $[Cd(NH_3)_6]^{2+}$ and the complex halides $[GeCl_6]^{2-}$ and $[SnCl_6]^{2-}$. It must be realized, however, that this is already a common feature of the chemistry of the elements of the second short period, where 6:co-ordinated complexes include the oxalate $[Al(C_2O_4)_3]^{3-}$ and the fluorides $[SiF_6]^{2-}$ and $[PF_6]^-$ and even the neutral molecule of the gas SF_6.

It is thus apparent that although the co-ordination chemistry of some elements may be satisfactorily explained in terms of the completion of inert-gas structures and the attainment of particular "effective atomic numbers", this simple approach is inadequate to provide a whole picture of co-ordination chemistry.

THE VALENCY-BOND THEORY[1]

In the Bohr atom the electrons are considered as occupying successive orbits at increasing distances from the atomic nucleus. In the quantum-mechanical description of the atom the electrons are placed in successive orbitals at increasing energy levels. These energy levels are defined by the quantum numbers, of which each electron in an atom has four:

(1)   A principal quantum number, $n = 1, 2, 3, \ldots$, corresponding (at least for the lowest values of n) to an orbit in the Bohr atom.

(2)   An azimuthal quantum number, $l = n - 1, n - 2, \ldots 0$, defining the angular momentum.

(3)   A magnetic quantum number, $m = \pm l, \pm l - 1, \pm l - 2, \ldots 0$, representing the components of l in the direction of a magnetic field.

(4)   A spin quantum number, $s = \pm \frac{1}{2}$.

The energy differences due to the third and fourth quantum numbers are comparatively small and in the free gaseous atoms, electrons differing only in these quantum numbers are found to have equal energies. This levelling out of the small energy differences is referred to as degeneracy. An energy-level diagram can now be drawn showing successive energy levels, due only to variation of the first two quantum numbers. For convenience of reference the orbitals so obtained are labelled with the principal quantum number and a letter representing the second quantum number, thus:

$l = 0$, s-orbitals; one orbital, two electrons;
$l = 1$, p-orbitals; three orbitals, six electrons;
$l = 2$, d-orbitals; five orbitals, ten electrons;
$l = 3$, f-orbitals; seven orbitals, fourteen electrons.

Large increases in energy level are apparent after the accommodation of 2, 10, 18, 36, 54 or 86 electrons — corresponding to the structures of the inert gases. The difference in phase between the number of electrons with successive principal quantum numbers (2, 8, 18, 32, . . .) and the number of elements in successive periods (2, 8, 8, 18, 18, 32, . . .) is due to the overlap of the energy levels of the *d-* and *f*-orbitals with one principal quantum number with those of the *s-* and *p*-orbitals of the next or next but one.

Vector Properties and Hybrid Bond Orbitals

The most important orbitals involved in chemical bonding are the *s-* and *p*-orbitals; *d*-orbitals are also involved when more than four bonds are formed by the same atom, but there is no conclusive evidence of *f*-orbitals being involved in bond formation.

The *s*-orbitals have spherical symmetry: electrons in these orbitals produce spherically-symmetrical regions of electron density, centred on the atomic nucleus. The *p*-orbitals, however, though spherically symmetrical as a group are not individually of spherical symmetry; electrons in these orbitals produce regions of electron density along cartesian axes originating at the

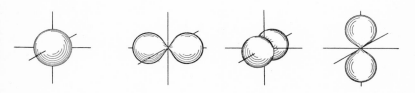

s-orbital   Set of three *p*-orbitals

atomic nucleus. If these *p*-orbitals are used in the formation of covalent bonds, the bound atoms will have to lie along these axes; that is to say, the bonds produced will be directed in space at angles of 90° to one another. A bond angle of 92° is in fact observed in hydrogen sulphide, in which a reasonable electronic structure involves two of the *p*-orbitals of the sulphur atom in bonding:

In the BX_3 compounds of boron the bonding is expected to involve one 2*s-* and two 2*p*-orbitals. This should lead to bond angles of 90° between

c

two B—X bonds, the third bond (that involving the 2s-orbital) being indeterminate in direction, the most probable position being that which bisects the re-entrant angle between the other bonds. In fact, all BX_3 molecules have plane equilateral triangular structures with bond angles of 120°:

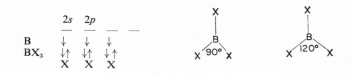

In the same way, the vector properties of the three 2p-orbitals and one 2s-orbital available would lead to a CX_4 molecule with three angles of 90°, whereas all CX_4 molecules are tetrahedral.

To account for these observations it is supposed that the electrons do not occupy ordinary atomic s- and p-orbitals, but that a new set of "hybrid-bond orbitals" is formed from the original atomic orbitals and that these impose a different stereochemistry. These "hybrid-bond orbital" systems are referred to by an appropriate combination of symbols, showing the atomic orbitals from which they are derived. Thus, the hybrid orbitals in the BX_3 molecules are referred to as a set of sp^2-orbitals and those in the CX_4 molecules as a set of sp^3-orbitals. The more common types of hybrid-bond orbitals and the stereochemistry imposed by them are as follows:

> two sp-orbitals, linear X—M—X;
> three sp^2-orbitals, plane equilateral triangular MX_3;
> four sp^3-orbitals, tetrahedral MX_4;
> six d^2sp^3-orbitals, octahedral MX_6;
> four dsp^2-orbitals, square planar MX_4;
> five dsp^3-orbitals, trigonal bipyramidal MX_5.

The tetrahedral configuration of the co-ordination compounds of the elements of the short periods and the B sub-groups now appears as a natura consequence of the availability of one s-orbital and three p-orbitals of the acceptor cation. Octahedral co-ordination becomes possible only when there are also available two d-orbitals. This occurs in the d^6-ions of the transition metals (Fe^{2+}, Co^{3+}, Pt^{4+}), the available d-orbitals (3d) having a principal quantum number one less than the s- and p-orbitals (4s, 4p); it also occurs in the second short period ($SiF_6{}^{2-}$, etc.), where the d-orbitals used (3d) have the same principal quantum number as the s- and p-orbitals (3s, 3p). The square planar co-ordination characteristic of the d^8 ions, Ni^{2+}, Pd^{2+}, Pt^{2+} and Au^{3+}, arises as the result of the use in hybrid-bond formation of the one available d-orbital to produce a set of dsp^2-orbitals.

Non-bonding Pairs: the Sidgwick–Powell Theory[2]

The simple MX_3 and MX_2 molecules of groups V and VI have permanent dipole moments indicating not only the polarity of the bonds but also the non-planarity or non-linearity of the molecules as a whole. The simplest explanation of this is that only the *p*-orbitals are involved in the bonding, leading to bond angles of about 90°, as observed in some of the hydrides, e.g.:

NH_3, 107°; PH_3, 94°; AsH_3, 92°; SbH_3, 91°; OH_2, 104°; SH_2, 92°

the higher bond angles in ammonia and water being attributed to repulsion of the hydrogen atoms attached to the small oxygen or nitrogen atoms.

In 1940, however, SIDGWICK and POWELL[3] pointed out that the stereo-chemistry of many molecules having non-bonding pairs of electrons could be explained on the assumption that *all* the electrons on the atom combined to form a set of hybrid-bond orbitals, only some of which were used for bonding; that is that the non-bonding pairs of electrons were also involved in the bond hybridization. In this case the MX_3 molecules of group V should be pyramidal, with bond angles of 109·5°. This idea is supported by the bond angles in NF_3 (102°) and $N(CH_3)_3$ (108°), which should be larger than those in ammonia if the bond angle of 107° is the result of mutual repulsion of the hydrogen atoms.

The decreasing bond angle in the series NH_3, PH_3, AsH_3, SbH_3 is now explained in terms of the repulsion of the bonding electrons (not the bound atoms), which will be closer to the central atom when this has a higher electronegativity; replacement of the hydrogen atoms of ammonia by fluorine atoms would withdraw the bonding electrons from the nitrogen atom, thus allowing the bond angle to become smaller[4].

There are a number of molecules with non-bonding electrons in which the octet is exceeded on the central atom and the Sidgwick–Powell theory is particularly successful in accounting for the stereochemistry of these. Thus, the peculiarly-distorted tetrahedral structures of the tetrahalides of selenium and tellurium are derived from the trigonal bipyramidal configuration enforced by dsp^3-hybridization, one of the equatorial pairs of electrons being non-bonding. The T-shaped molecule of chlorine trifluoride is similarly derived from a trigonal bipyramid with two vacant equatorial positions:

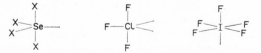

The very unusual square pyramidal molecule of iodine pentafluoride is similarly derived from an octahedron with one vacant position.

Paramagnetism[5]

The transition metals are distinguished from the metals of the short periods by their readiness to form cations without the loss of all their valency electrons. Thus the divalent cations typical of the transition metals of the first long period arise by the loss of the two 4s-electrons, leaving a partly-filled group of 3d-orbitals. According to Hund's principle of maximum multiplicity, the electrons in these orbitals remain, as far as possible, unpaired and with parallel spins.

Since atoms with unpaired electrons possess a permanent magnetic moment, many transition-metal compounds are paramagnetic, that is they tend to move into an applied magnetic field. The paramagnetic susceptibility due to uncompensated electron spins is given by:

$$\mu = \sqrt{[4S(S + 1)]} \tag{1}$$

where S is the sum of the spin quanta; and as each electron has a spin quantum of $\pm \frac{1}{2}$, this can be expressed as:

$$\mu = \sqrt{[n(n + 2)]} \tag{2}$$

where n is the number of electrons with uncompensated spins.

Experimentally the magnetic susceptibility, χ, is usually determined on a Gouy balance: this is an ordinary chemical balance, so arranged that the powdered or dissolved specimen can be hung below one of the balance pans in a small tube; the lower end of this tube lies between the poles of a powerful magnet and the upper end far enough from the poles of the magnet for the magnetic field to be comparatively insignificant. The specimen is weighed with and without the magnet in position and the molar paramagnetic susceptibility calculated from the equation:

$$\chi_M = \left(kv + \frac{2gv \cdot dw}{AH^2}\right) \frac{M}{W} \tag{3}$$

where k is the volume susceptibility of the medium, v the volume of the specimen, g the acceleration due to gravity, A the cross-sectional area of the specimen, H the magnetic field strength, W the weight of the specimen, dw the difference between the weighings and M its molecular weight.

As the susceptibility and the magnetic moment are related by the equation:

$$\chi_M = \frac{N^2\mu^2}{3RT}$$

the magnetic moment of the paramagnetic atom is given by:

$$\mu = \sqrt{(3RT\chi_M)/N} \tag{4}$$

where N is Avogadro's number, and T the absolute temperature (though closer agreement with experimental results is observed if T is measured from an experimental zero, known as the Curie temperature).

In practice most transition metal compounds are "magnetically dilute", that is the atom with a permanent magnetic moment is surrounded by other atoms without any permanent moment. This prevents any possibility of interaction between neighbouring magnetic atoms, but as all atoms with paired electrons are slightly diamagnetic (i.e. tend to move out of a magnetic field), it is necessary to correct the experimentally-determined susceptibility for the combined effect of the diamagnetism of all the atoms in the compound. This correction is comparatively small but may sometimes amount to about a quarter of the total so cannot be ignored. Replacement of χ_M in equation (4) by the corrected susceptibility, $\chi_{M'}$, now gives the "effective magnetic moment" of the paramagnetic atom:

$$\mu_{\text{eff}} = \sqrt{(3RT\chi_{M'})}/N$$
$$= 2 \cdot 84\sqrt{(T\chi_{M'})} \tag{5}$$

where the values of μ_{eff} in equation (5) are in Bohr magnetons (β) and correspond to those expected from equations (1) or (2). Some of the theoretical and observed values of μ_{eff} are given in the following table, which refers to aqueous solutions of the ions:

THEORETICAL AND OBSERVED VALUES OF μ_{eff}

Cations	Electronic structure 3d					Unpaired electrons	β theory	β observed
V^{3+}	↓	↓				2	2·83	2·76–2·85
Cr^{3+}, V^{2+}	↓	↓	↓			3	3·88	3·8–3·9
Mn^{3+}, Cr^{2+}	↓	↓	↓	↓		4	4·90	4·8–4·9
Fe^{3+}, Mn^{2+}	↓	↓	↓	↓	↓	5	5·91	5·8–5·9
Fe^{2+}	↓↑	↓	↓	↓	↓	4	4·90	5·26
Co^{2+}	↓↑	↓↑	↓	↓	↓	3	3·88	5·0
Ni^{2+}	↓↑	↓↑	↓↑	↓	↓	2	2·83	3·4
Cu^{2+}	↓↑	↓↑	↓↑	↓↑	↓	1	1·73	2·0
Zn^{2+}, Cu^{+}	↓↑	↓↑	↓↑	↓↑	↓↑	0	0	0

It will be seen that agreement between the theoretical and observed values is excellent in the ions containing up to five electrons, but that abnormally-high values of magnetic moment are observed in the ions with from six to nine electrons. The reason for this is not fully understood. One possibility is that a small proportion of these ions is in an excited state, one or more of the paired 3d-electrons being promoted to a higher orbital such as the 4s-, 4p- or 4d-orbitals.

The theoretical magnetic moments in the table above are calculated on the "spin only" basis of equation (1), but it is also possible for a contribution to the magnetic moment to be made by uncompensated magnetic quantum numbers. In a d-set of orbitals these may have the values ± 2, ± 1 or 0, so that a d^1-ion would have two quanta of orbital magnetic moment in addition to the spin moment already mentioned. In the same way a d^2-ion would have $2 + 1 = 3$ quanta of orbital moment, a d^3-ion $2 + 1 + 0 = 3$ quanta, a d^4-ion $2 + 1 + 0 - 1 = 2$ quanta and so on. In the same way as the spin quanta combine to give a magnetic moment according to equation (1) above, the magnetic moment due to the orbital contribution is given by:

$$\mu = \sqrt{[L(L + 1)]}$$

The overall magnetic moment of any paramagnetic atom is thus given by a combination of the spin and orbital contributions, and as these may interact with one another no universally-applicable formula can be given for its calculation. In the transition metals of the first long period, however, the orbital contribution is almost completely quenched so that the experimental values of the magnetic moments correspond very closely to spin-only values. The correspondence is often less satisfactory in the second and third long periods, and in the rare-earth elements, where paramagnetism arises from an incomplete $4f$-shell, the orbital contribution is large.

There is some evidence that the orbital contribution varies slightly with changes in the stereochemical environment of the atom; this has been applied particularly to the compounds of divalent cobalt and nickel, which seem to fall into groups on the basis of magnetic data, and can be expected to exhibit two stereochemical configurations in each case. In a number of octahedrally-co-ordinated cobaltous complexes, for example, such as the hydrate $[Co(OH_2)_6]^{2+}$ or ammine $[Co(NH_3)_6]^{2+}$, magnetic moments are observed between 4·9 and 5·0, whereas the tetrahedrally-co-ordinated $[CoCl_4]^{2-}$ ion (4·74) or $[Co(SCN)_4]^{2-}$ ion (4·33) have considerably lower moments.

When a transition metal cation is co-ordinated, some of the d-orbitals may be required for bond formation; the non-bonding d-electrons must then be confined to the remaining d-orbitals; this enforces pairing and the paramagnetic susceptibility is correspondingly reduced. Thus the complex cyanides of the Fe^{2+}, Co^{3+}, Pt^{4+} and Ni^{2+} ions are diamagnetic and in the ferricyanides the susceptibility of the iron atom is reduced to $2·0\ \beta$ corresponding to one unpaired electron.

	3d					4s	4p			
Fe^{2+}, Co^{3+}	↓↑	↓	↓	↓	↓					
$[Fe(CN)_6]^{4-}$ ⎫	↓↑	↓↑	↓↑	↓↑	↓↑	↓↑	↓↑	↓↑	↓↑	d^2sp^3
$[Co(CN)_6]^{3-}$ ⎭				CN	CN	CN	CN	CN	CN	hybrid bonds
$[Fe(CN)_6]^{3-}$	↓↑	↓↑	↓	↓↑	↓↑	↓↑	↓↑	↓↑	↓↑	d^2sp^3-bonds,
				CN	CN	CN	CN	CN	CN	one unpaired electron
Ni^{2+}	↓↑	↓↑	↓↑	↓	↓					
$[Ni(CN)_4]^{2-}$	↓↑	↓↑	↓↑	↓↑	↓↑	↓↑	↓↑	↓↑		dsp^2
					CN	CN	CN	CN		hybrid bonds

In some circumstances the magnetic susceptibility provides useful evidence for the detailed structure of the compound concerned. Thus, treatment of potassium ferrocyanide with nitric acid gives the deep red nitroprusside, $K_2[Fe(CN)_5(NO)]$, long considered to be a nitroso derivative of ferric iron. The nitroprussides, however, are diamagnetic and must be considered as derivatives of ferrous iron, the odd electron of the nitric oxide molecule having been transferred to the iron atom:

	3d					4s	4p		
$[Fe^{III}(CN)_5(NO)]^{2-}$	⇅	⇅	↓	⇅	⇅	⇅	⇅	⇅	⇅
			·NO	CN		CN	CN	CN	CN
$[Fe^{II}(CN)_5(NO^+)]^{2-}$	⇅	⇅	⇅	⇅	⇅	⇅	⇅	⇅	⇅
			NO	CN		CN	CN	CN	CN

Another example of the value of measurements of magnetic susceptibility is the demonstration of the double formula for hypophosphoric acid and its salts. The empirical formula, H_2PO_3, would lead to a paramagnetic molecule whereas the hypophosphates are diamagnetic.

The Magnetic Criterion of Bond Type: Inner- and Outer-orbital Complexes

Among the complex salts of iron and cobalt are some with abnormal magnetic properties. Thus, the complex fluorides, $K_3[FeF_6]$ and $K_3[CoF_6]$, have high magnetic susceptibilities, corresponding to the presence of five and four unpaired electrons, respectively, as in the free metal cations. Pauling explained these high numbers of unpaired electrons by suggesting that in these complexes the Fe—F and Co—F bonds were electrostatic, not covalent as in most complex salts. In this way it is possible to use magnetic properties as a criterion of bond type, so long as the free metal cation has from four to seven electrons in the d-shell; with less than four or more than seven d-electrons there is no distinction in the magnetic properties between the covalent and ionic complexes.

This idea that the bonds in the complex ion are ionic does not accord well with the familiar suppression of ferric ion concentration produced by fluorides (for example the decolorization of ferric thiocyanate solutions), nor with the properties of the ferrioxalates[6], which also have high magnetic susceptibilities: the ferrioxalates can be resolved into optical isomers and show the absorption band in the infra-red at 1730 cm⁻¹, characteristic of carboxyl groups in esters. The ferrioxalates, however, are markedly more reactive than the diamagnetic (and therefore "covalent") cobaltioxalates, rhodioxalates and iridioxalates: these diamagnetic complexes are highly resistant to hydrolysis, ferrioxalates are rapidly hydrolysed, even by boiling water; the racemization of the optical isomers of the diamagnetic oxalates is very slow, that of ferrioxalates rapid in dilute solutions of alkali oxalates; ferrioxalates exchange rapidly in solution with radioactive oxalate ions, cobaltioxalates at an immeasurably slow rate.

This conflict between the magnetic and other evidence may be resolved by the suggestion that in the complexes with high magnetic susceptibilities the bonding is covalent, but involves the outer d-orbitals ($4d$) of the iron or cobalt atom, leaving the maximum number of unpaired electrons in the inner ($3d$) orbitals. In this case the hybrid bond orbitals are derived from the $4s$-, $4p$- and $4d$-atomic orbitals, instead of the usual $4s$-, $4p$- and $3d$-atomic orbitals[7]:

	3d					4s	4p			4d					
Fe³⁺	↓	↓	↓	↓	↓										
[Fe(CN)₆]³⁻	↓↑	↓↑	↓	↓↑ CN	↓↑ CN	↓↑ CN	↓↑ CN	↓↑ CN	↓↑ CN						"inner-orbital"
[FeF₆]³⁻ or [Fe(Ox)₃]³⁻	↓	↓	↓	↓	↓	↓↑ X	↓↑ X	↓↑ X	↓↑ X	↓↑ X	↓↑ X				"outer-orbital"
Co³⁺	↓↑	↓	↓	↓	↓										
[CoF₆]³⁻	↓↑	↓	↓	↓	↓	↓↑ F	↓↑ F	↓↑ F	↓↑ F	↓↑ F	↓↑ F				"outer-orbital"
[Co(Ox)₃]³⁻ or [Co(NH₃)₆]³⁺	↓↑	↓↑	↓↑	↓↑ X	↓↑ X	↓↑ X	↓↑ X	↓↑ X	↓↑ X						"inner-orbital"

This method of resolving the conflict was considered by Pauling[1], but rejected by him on the grounds that the extra energy required to bring into use the outer d-orbitals was too great. That "outer-orbital" bond-hybridization is permissible, however, can be seen from the formation of 6:co-ordinated complexes of zinc and cadmium (for example, the ammines $[M(NH_3)_6]^{2+}$), and the formation of clearly covalent compounds such as SF_6 by elements in the second short period. In this respect, it is interesting that the complex oxalates of aluminium, $[Al(C_2O_4)_3]^{3-}$, in which there is no alternative to "outer-orbital" bonding ($3s$, $3p^3$, $3d^2$), show the characteristic infra-red absorption at 1730 cm⁻¹, and resemble the ferri-oxalates in being readily hydrolysed, rapidly racemized and undergoing rapid exchange with labelled oxalate ions.

Conversely, the chromioxalates, for which magnetic evidence is of no value (Cr^{3+} is a $3d^3$-ion), resemble the cobaltioxalates in general lack of reactivity and presumably have "inner-orbital" bond hybridization.

Amongst the diamagnetic "inner-orbital" complexes of trivalent cobalt is the hydrate, which must thus be considered a true co-ordination compound

$[Co(OH_2)_6]^{3+}$. There is much other evidence that water of hydration of the transition metal cations is in fact co-ordinated, for example the isomerism in the chromic chloride hydrates (p. 5) and the square-planar location of the molecules of water in hydrated cupric salts (p. 34). Thus, it is now widely accepted that the high magnetic susceptibilities in aqueous solution of all the transition metal cations of the first long period, except Co^{3+}, are due to the presence of these ions in the form of 6:co-ordinated complex hydrates, with "outer-orbital" bond hybridization and it is doubtful whether any cases are known of these ions occurring in the "free" state, even in anhydrous crystals.

THE LIGAND-FIELD THEORY[2, 8]

Despite the success of Pauling's valence-bond theory in interpreting the main features of co-ordination chemistry, there are a number of aspects of which it does not give a satisfactory explanation. Outstanding among these difficulties is the peculiar behaviour of the ions of divalent nickel, palladium and platinum and trivalent gold (d^8-ions), which apparently do not form the expected 5:co-ordinated complexes. The valence-bond theory is able to propose a form of bond hybridization (dsp^2) suitable for the square-planar structures, but this does not explain why this structure is preferred to other possible stereochemical configurations, such as tetrahedral or the 5:co-ordinated trigonal bipyramid (which does in fact occur in iron carbonyl, a complex of a zero valent d^8-atom). The formation of square-planar cupric complexes, involving dsp^2 bond hybridization and the promotion of one electron from the $3d$-orbital to some higher level, is another weakness, and the Pauling theory offers no explanation as to why the "outer-orbital" type of bond hybridization is preferred in some complexes.

Based on the crystal field theory of BETHE (1929) and VAN VLECK (1931–1935), another approach, known as the ligand-field theory, has recently proved remarkably successful in explaining these and some other difficulties.

The ligand-field theory is an electrostatic approach, regarding a complex as consisting of a central cation, surrounded by a cage of anions (or the negative ends of dipolar molecules). The theory is concerned primarily with the effect of this environment on the energies of the d-orbitals of the cation. The five d-orbitals must be considered separately instead of as a group. This theory thus bears a similar relationship to the Pauling theory as that did to the simple octet approach — yet another quantum number is considered in detail.

The Effect of the Ligand-field on the d-orbitals

The d-orbitals differ from the p-orbitals in not being all alike: three of these orbitals (the d_{xy}, d_{xz} and d_{yz}) resemble one another in producing regions of electron density in the three planes of cartesian axes, but directed between these axes:

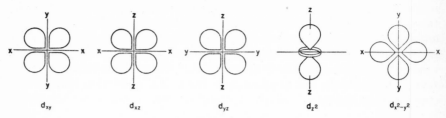

The other two differ from these three and from one another: the $d_{x^2-y^2}$-orbital produces regions of electron density along the x- and y-axes; the d_{z^2}-orbital produces most of its electron density along the z-axis, with a small proportion in the form of an annulus in the xy-plane. The d_{xy}-, d_{xz}- and d_{yz}-orbitals together form a set with spherical symmetry and the $d_{x^2-y^2}$ and d_{z^2} together form another set with spherical symmetry, but these two sets of orbitals are affected differently by their environment.

In an octahedral complex ligands lie along the x-, y- and z-axes. The electrostatic repulsion between these ligands and the electrons of the central cation will be much greater if these electrons are in the $d_{x^2-y^2}$- or d_{z^2}-orbitals than if they are in the d_{xy}-, d_{xz}- or d_{yz}-orbitals; hence the d-orbitals, which are degenerate (i.e. all of equal energy) in the "free" ion are split into two groups, the energy of the $d_{x^2-y^2}$- and d_{z^2}-orbitals being increased far more by the presence of ligands lying along the axes on which these orbitals produce their regions of maximum electron density:

In a tetrahedral complex, it is the d_{xy}-, d_{xz}-, and d_{yz}-orbitals which produce their regions of maximum electron density in the direction nearest the ligands and the above splitting of the d-orbitals is reversed:

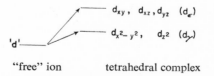

Other symmetries of the ligands lead to more complicated subdivisions of the d-orbital energy levels. Several nomenclatures have been proposed for these different energy levels; that which will be used here refers to the d_{xy}-, d_{xz}- and d_{yz}-orbitals as d_ε (other usages are t_{2g} and γ_5), and the $d_{x^2-y^2}$- and d_{z^2}- orbitals as d_γ (other usages are e_g and γ_3).

One of the results of the comparatively small energy difference between the subdivided d-orbitals is that electronic transitions from the lower to the higher group can be brought about by the absorption of visible light. This leads to the complex compounds appearing coloured. Observation of the frequency of the absorbed light and application of the Einstein equation relating the frequency and energy:

$$E = Nh\nu$$

is the most satisfactory method of determining the energy difference between the sets of d-orbitals. Thus, in aqueous solution the $3d^1$-titanous ion, $[Ti(OH_2)_6]^{3+}$, has a single absorption band reaching maximum intensity at 500 mμ, equivalent to a transition energy of about 60 kcal/g-ion; the transition may be represented as follows:

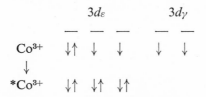

When there are several electrons in the d-orbitals the number of possible transitions is greater and the absorption spectrum is correspondingly more complicated, but the low-intensity absorption in the visible or near ultra-violet or infra-red regions, typical of the transition metal cations, is due to transitions of this type. In the lanthanide series corresponding transitions occur within the $4f$-orbitals, the degeneracy of which is likewise removed in the presence of an electrostatic field.

The comparatively small energy separations between the different d-orbitals are of the same order of magnitude as the energy required to force electrons with uncompensated spins into doubly-filled orbitals, for example:

	$3d\varepsilon$			$3d\gamma$	
Co^{3+}	↓↑	↓	↓	↓	↓
↓					
$*Co^{3+}$	↓↑	↓↑	↓↑		

It is thus apparent that in octahedral complexes of cations with more than three d-electrons, there are two energy considerations acting in direct opposition to one another: in order to maintain the maximum multiplicity condition energy must be supplied to some of the electrons to promote them to the upper d_γ-level; alternatively, in order to avoid this promotion, energy must be provided to enforce pairing of the electrons in the lower d_ε-level.

"High-spin" and "Low-spin" Complexes

In octahedral complexes the "separation energy" between the d_ε- and d_γ-orbitals (Δ) and the "pairing energy" (Π) are opposed only when the number of electrons in the d-shell is four, five, six or seven. The two possible configurations can be distinguished by their magnetic susceptibilities as can be seen in the following examples:

Total d-electrons	Typical ion	Low-spin form d_ε		d_γ	No. odd	High-spin form d_ε		d_γ		No. odd
3	Cr^{3+}	↓ ↓ ↓			3	↓ ↓ ↓				3
4	Mn^{3+}	↓↑ ↓	↓		2	↓ ↓ ↓		↓		4
5	Fe^{3+}	↓↑ ↓↑	↓		1	↓ ↓ ↓		↓ ↓		5
6	Co^{3+}	↓↑ ↓↑	↓↑		0	↓↑ ↓ ↓		↓ ↓		4
7	Co^{2+}	↓↑ ↓↑	↓↑	↓	1	↓↑ ↓↑ ↓		↓ ↓		3
8	Ni^{2+}	↓↑ ↓↑	↓↑	↓ ↓	2	↓↑ ↓↑ ↓↑		↓ ↓		2

The condition which determines which of these configurations is taken up in any particular complex ion is the relative magnitudes of the "separation energy", Δ, and the "pairing energy", Π. If Δ is greater than Π, the low-spin form will be expected and if Π is greater than Δ, the high-spin. The low-spin form of the ion will have available the d_γ-orbitals for the formation of hybrid bond orbitals and so form "inner orbital" complexes; in the high-spin form, these d_γ-orbitals are occupied and "outer orbital" bonding is the result.

It may be noted that in the valency-bond theory it is the nature of the bonding in the complex which determines the distribution of the d-electrons; in the ligand-field theory, the position is reversed. The factors which control the configuration to be adopted are now:

(a) The "pairing energy", Π, which is not much affected by changes of the ligand and is of the same order in the $3d$-, $4d$- and $5d$-orbitals.

(b) The orbital "separation energy", Δ, dependent on the ligand-field and consequently sensitive to changes of the ligand. Irrespective of the cation involved, the values of Δ have been found to increase in the same order, viz.:

$$I^- < Br^- < Cl^- < F^- < H_2O < C_2O_4^{2-} < NH_3 < en < NO_2^- < CN^-$$

The following table gives the observed values of Δ and Π for some transition metal cations in aqueous solution (determined spectroscopically); the energy is in kilocalories per gramme-ion. In every case Π is considerably larger than Δ, except for the Co^{3+} ion, for which Π and Δ are nearly equal. We should expect all these hydrated ions to have the high-spin configuration as all do, except the $[Co(OH_2)_6]^{3+}$ ion, which is diamagnetic, though the complex fluoride, for which Δ is only slightly smaller, has the high-spin configuration. The much larger difference between Π and Δ in the hydrated ferric ion is reflected in the high-spin configuration of the fluoride, hydrate, oxalate and ammonia complexes.

No. of d-electrons	Ion M^{2+}	Δ	Π	Ion M^{3+}	Δ	Π
4	Cr^{2+}	41	69	Mn^{3+}	61	80
5	Mn^{2+}	23	75	Fe^{3+}	40	84
6	Fe^{2+}	30	51	Co^{3+}	52	60
7	Co^{2+}	27	66			

In the second and third long periods the values of Π are not much different, but those of Δ are considerably larger, so that in all known complexes Δ is greater than Π and the low-spin configuration is adopted.

THE LIGAND-FIELD THEORY AND STEREOCHEMISTRY[2, 8, 9]

In the d^{10}-ions, typical of the B sub-group metals, the electrons in the d-shell possess overall spherical symmetry; spherical symmetry also occurs in the low-spin d^6-complexes of the Co^{3+} and Fe^{2+} ions, the high-spin complexes of the d^5-ions, Mn^{2+} and Fe^{3+} and in the d^3-complexes of trivalent chromium. In almost all other cases the d-orbital electrons are distributed asymmetrically and this has some important stereochemical consequences, particularly in the following examples:

Divalent Cobalt

Most cobaltous complexes with ligands producing low-strength fields (F^-, OH_2, etc.) are octahedral, with magnetic susceptibility corresponding to three unpaired electrons; the octahedral structure has been confirmed by X-ray analysis of the ammines $[Co(NH_3)_6]^{2+}$.

	3d	4s	4p	4d
Co^{2+}	↓↑ ↓↑ ↓ ↓ ↓			
$[Co(NH_3)_6]^{2+}$	↓↑ ↓↑ ↓ ↓ ↓	↓↑	↓↑ ↓↑ ↓↑	↓↑ ↓↑
$[Co(CN)_6]^{4-}$	↓↑ ↓↑ ↓↑ ↓↑ ↓↑	↓↑	↓↑ ↓↑ ↓↑	↓

With ligands producing a high field, such as cyanide, however, a difficulty arises as it is impossible to form "inner orbital" complexes of the Co^{2+} ion without promotion of one of the 3d-electrons to a higher level (4d or 5s?). This results in the very powerful reducing action of complexes such as the cobaltocyanides, which even decompose water with the evolution of hydrogen:

$$[Co(CN)_6]^{4-} - \bar{e} = [Co(CN)_6]^{3-} \qquad E^\circ = -0.8 \text{ V}$$

The Co^{2+} ion is clearly unsuitable for the formation of octahedral complexes with such ligands. It is, however, unusually well suited to the formation of tetrahedral complexes, since the tetrahedral ligand-field causes splitting of the d-orbitals into a lower set of two and an upper set of three and the seven electrons can be paired in the lower set and unpaired in the upper:

	$3d\gamma$	$3d\varepsilon$	$4s$	$4p$
$[CoCl_4]^{2-}$	↓↑ ↓↑	↓ ↓ ↓	↓↑	↓↑ ↓↑ ↓↑

The tetrahedral structure is common in cobaltous complexes. Thus, although all the ferrithiocyanates are 6:co-ordinated, those of divalent cobalt are 4:co-ordinated, $[Co(SCN)_4]^{2-}$; a 4:co-ordinated acetylacetone derivative is known, monomeric in the vapour phase; and tetrahedral $[CoCl_4]^{2-}$ ions have been demonstrated by the X-ray analysis of Cs_2CoCl_4[10] and Cs_3CoCl_5[11] (which also has free Cl^- ions).

In all of these compounds the Co^{2+} ion has a magnetic susceptibility above 4β (corresponding to three unpaired electrons and a variable orbital contribution), but a few Co^{2+} compounds have lower moments (about 2β) and are usually regarded as square planar. There does not, however, appear to be any unequivocally established example of square planar co-ordination for divalent cobalt. A recent X-ray analysis of the metastable, violet form of the compound $Co(C_5H_5N)_2Cl_2$ suggests that the trans-planar arrangement of the ligands becomes octahedral by polymerization (compare $CuCl_2.2OH_2$, p. 34)[11a].

The d^8-ions, Ni^{2+}, Pd^{2+}, Pt^{2+} and Au^{3+}

The valence-bond treatment of the square-planar complexes of these ions relates the stereochemistry to the use of dsp^2-hybrid bond orbitals by the central atom, resulting in the complete pairing of the electrons, as shown by the diamagnetism of the complexes.

In terms of the ligand-field theory, the d-orbitals in a square-planar ligand field, are split into four sub-levels:

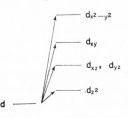

The $d_{x^2-y^2}$-orbital, which points directly towards the ligands, has a very high energy, and the d_{z^2}-orbital, which points in the directions normal to the plane of the ligands, has the lowest energy; the eight d-electrons are paired in the four lowest orbitals, the $d_{x^2-y^2}$-orbital remaining empty. This arrangement results in regions of very high electron density in directions normal to the plane of the complex and hence to the repulsion of further ligands, which might approach to complete the octahedral structure. The square-planar structure is thus stabilized; the stabilization is expected to be greatest for the highest ligand-fields and the greatest orbital separation energies. We thus find that this configuration is adopted almost exclusively by the Pd^{2+}, Pt^{2+} and Au^{3+} ions, for which the orbital separation energies are larger than in the first long period.

The square-planar configuration is adopted by the Ni^{2+} ion in complexes with high ligand-fields, for instance the complex cyanide, $[Ni(CN)_4]^{2-}$, the dithio-oxalate, $[Ni(C_2O_2S_2)_2]^{2-}$ (both confirmed by X-ray analysis[12, 13]), and most of the inner complexes of organic chelates, such as the glyoximes and salicylaldoxime (II); all are diamagnetic, as is the phthalocyanin, in which the planar structure is an inevitable consequence of the molecular structure as a whole.

With those ligands which produce a weaker field, however, the Ni^{2+} ion forms octahedral complexes. Familiar examples are the hydrate, $[Ni(OH_2)_6]^{2+}$, hexammine, $[Ni(NH_3)_6]^{2+}$, and complex nitrite, $[Ni(NO_2)_6]^{4-}$ (all of which have been shown to form salts with the K_2PtCl_6 structure[14, 15]) and the tris-dipyridyl salts, $[Ni(dipy)_3]^{2+}$, which have been resolved into optical isomers[16]. In these octahedral complexes, the symmetry of the ligand field splits the $3d$-orbitals into two sets ($d\varepsilon$ and $d\gamma$) and causes the two $d\gamma$-electrons to be distributed between the two $d\gamma$-orbitals, so that the compounds are paramagnetic and coloured (usually blue-green, due to $d\varepsilon$–$d\gamma$-transitions). The ligands must thus be attached by "outer orbital", sp^3d^2-bonds:

	$3d\varepsilon$			$3d\gamma$		$4s$		$4p$				$4d$		
Ni^{2+}	↓↑	↓↑	↓↑	↓	↓									
$[Ni(NH_3)_6]^{2+}$	↓↑	↓↑	↓↑	↓	↓	↓↑		↓↑	↓↑	↓↑		↓↑	↓↑	
						NH_3		NH_3	NH_3	NH_3		NH_3	NH_3	

With the ligand o-phenylene-bis-dimethylarsine (diarsine) nickel and palladium form isomorphous iodides, $[M(diarsine)_2]I_2$; the palladium compound has been shown by X-ray analysis to have a structure in which the Pd^{2+} ion is surrounded by four arsenic atoms in a plane, at distances appropriate for the Pd—As single bond (2·38 Å), and two iodine atoms normal to the plane at very long distances (3·52 Å, theory for the Pd—I single bond 2·65 Å), but so close that some form of bonding must occur; these compounds are diamagnetic and it is suggested that the M—I bonds may be linear pd-hybrids[17]. A somewhat similar situation arises in the compound

$CsAuCl_3$, apparently a complex halide of divalent gold, but shown, by its isomorphism with the compound $Cs_2AgAuCl_6$, to contain gold in both the uni- and tri-valent states. X-ray analysis of these compounds has shown that the Au^+ or Ag^+ ions are linearly 2:co-ordinated and the Au^{3+} ions at the centre of a square of chloride ions[18]; these two types of complex ions are arranged so that the chlorine atoms of $AuCl_2^-$ or $AgCl_2^-$ ions also complete elongated octahedral co-ordination of the Au^{3+} ions, which have an environment of four chlorine atoms in a plane at a distance of 2·42 Å (i.e. Au—Cl single bonds) and two more, normal to this plane at a distance of 3·13 Å, a distance too short to allow for complete separation of the atoms (I):

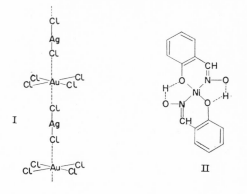

The structure of the diarsine complexes indicates that the transition from the square-planar to octahedral co-ordination, which depends on the field strength produced by the ligands, is not necessarily sharp, although magnetic evidence will distinguish between symmetrical octahedral co-ordination on the one hand and planar or unsymmetrical octahedral co-ordination on the other. In some cases extremely small differences in chemical structure are responsible for a change in configuration. Thus, the salicylaldoxime complex (II) is yellow and diamagnetic in benzene solution and in the solid state, and has been shown to be planar by X-ray analysis[13], but its solution in pyridine is blue and paramagnetic, probably because solvent molecules are completing octahedral co-ordination. Similarly, two series of bis-ethylene-diamine complexes are known[19]: some, such as the salt $[Ni(en)_2][AgIBr]_2$, are yellow and diamagnetic, while others, such as the sulphate, $[Ni(en)_2](SO_4)$, and perchlorate are blue and paramagnetic, possibly because of completion of octahedral co-ordination by the oxygen atoms of the oxy-acid anions, as in the crystal of copper sulphate pentahydrate (see p. 34).

An alternative solution to the problem of these blue, paramagnetic, 4:co-ordinated compounds is that they may involve tetrahedral co-ordination of the Ni^{2+} ion. This cannot be distinguished from octahedral co-ordination by magnetic measurements, but the asymmetry of the electrons in a tetra-hedral environment should lead to a distorted tetrahedral structure:

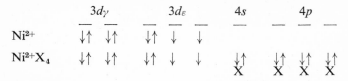

The tetrahedral configuration was first proposed by Pauling to account for the paramagnetism of the blue $[Ni(NH_3)_4]^{2+}$ salts, but it has never been confirmed in any of these by X-ray analysis and in at least one instance, the nitrite, it seems more likely that these compounds should be represented as octahedral inner salts, $[Ni(NH_3)_4(NO_2)_2]^0$. The acetylacetonate, $[Ni(acac)_2]^0$, is another example of this sort but has been shown to be trimeric in organic solvents and in the solid state[20], presumably with octahedral co-ordination. A series of phosphine complexes, $[Ni(PR_3)_2X_2]^0$, has been found to be monomeric in benzene solution and so presumably tetrahedral and this has been confirmed by X-ray analysis, which indicates a distorted tetrahedral structure[21]. It is clear that only by X-ray analysis can the structures of these apparently 4:co-ordinated, paramagnetic com-pounds be finally decided.

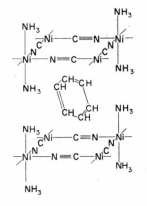

III

The stereochemistry of divalent nickel is well exemplified in the structure[22] of the remarkable compound $Ni(CN)_2.NH_3.C_6H_6$, formed when benzene vapour is passed into ammoniacal nickel cyanide solution and at one time used as a method of estimating benzene in gases. In this compound the Ni^{2+} and CN^- ions form a planar network, alternate Ni^{2+} ions being co-ordinated by four carbon or four nitrogen atoms of the CN^- ions; the Ni^{2+} ions attached to four carbon atoms are square-planar co-ordinated as in the complex cyanide, but those attached to four cyanide groups through

D

the nitrogen atoms have the octahedral configuration completed by co-ordination of ammonia molecules above and below the plane of the network; the benzene molecules are trapped in holes in the lattice and can be replaced by other molecules of similar dimensions (III).

Cupric Complexes

The valency-bond treatment of the square-planar complexes of the d^9 Cu²⁺ ion is unsatisfactory in two main respects: firstly, the use of dsp^2-hybrid bond orbitals necessitates the "promotion" of one of the $3d$-electrons to a higher level; this should lead to ready loss of this electron by oxidation to Cu³⁺, a process which occurs only with great difficulty; secondly, detailed X-ray analysis of many cupric compounds has shown that only rarely is the co-ordination truly square-planar, the more usual arrangement being a form of octahedral co-ordination with two bonds considerably longer than the other four*, for example:

Copper sulphate, the only divalent transition metal sulphate not belonging to the series of isomorphous heptahydrates, crystallizes at ordinary tempera-ture as the pentahydrate, $CuSO_4.5H_2O$. In the crystal each Cu²⁺ ion is surrounded by four water molecules at the corners of a square and two, more distant, oxygen atoms (belonging to sulphate anions) completing an elongated octahedron (IV); the fifth water molecule is not co-ordinated to the copper ion but links the sulphate anions and co-ordinated water molecules by hydrogen bonds[23].

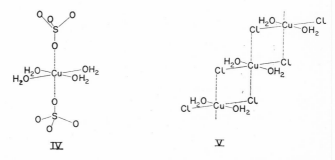

IV   V

In crystalline cupric chloride dihydrate[24] there are square-planar molecules of $[Cu(OH_2)_2Cl_2]^0$, so arranged that the chlorine atoms of one molecule fall just above or below the copper atoms of another (V), each copper atom having an environment of two OH₂ molecules (Cu—O distance 2·01 Å) and two chloride ions in a plane (Cu—Cl, 2·31 Å) with two more distant chloride ions above and below (Cu—Cl, 2·98 Å), completing the elongated octahedral co-ordination. A similar arrangement occurs in the double salts, $CuCl_2$.

---

* Gradually accumulating evidence, both by X-ray analysis and by studies in solution, suggests, however, that Cu²⁺ ions may frequently be 5:co-ordinated.

$2KCl.2OH_2$ and $CuBr_2.2NH_4Br.2OH_2$, each copper atom being surrounded by two water molecules and two halide ions in a plane with two further, more distant, halide ions above and below.

In anhydrous cupric chloride[25] (and bromide) the copper and chlorine atoms are arranged in chains so that each copper atom is at the centre of a square of chlorine atoms (VI). A similar arrangement is adopted in the halides of divalent palladium and platinum (see p. 45), but there is a significant difference between the $CuCl_2$ structure and that of these halides: in $CuCl_2$ the chains are so packed in the crystal that the chlorine atoms forming part of one chain also complete elongated octahedral co-ordination of the copper atoms in neighbouring chains (VIa, VII), whereas in the $PdCl_2$ structure the chains are packed as if they were organic molecules and the palladium atoms have true square-planar co-ordination (VIII).

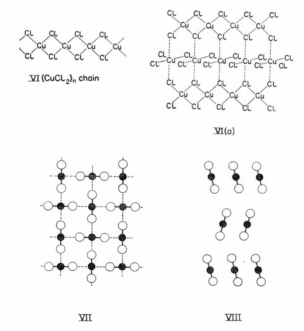

VI $(CuCl_2)_n$ chain

VI(a)

VII   VIII

End view, showing packing of the MX_2 flat chains in cupric (VII) and palladous (VIII) halides

There is no sort of hybrid bond system which can account for this peculiar type of co-ordination, but it is a natural consequence of the Ligand-field treatment of the d^9-ion: In an octahedral environment an ion with nine d-electrons would have three electrons in the $d\gamma$-shell over a full, spherically-symmetrical $d\varepsilon$-group; if electron pairing occurred mainly in the $d_{x^2-y^2}$-orbital, the electron density in the x- and y-axes would be higher than in the

z-axis and the four groups along these axes would be further from the copper atom owing to the greater repulsion; alternatively, if pairing occurred mainly in the d_{z^2}-orbital, then the two groups along the z-axis would be correspondingly repelled, the situation actually observed. In extreme cases these two groups might be lost, the copper atom becoming truly square-planar co-ordinated; in this case we should expect eight of the nine electrons to be paired in the four orbitals of lowest energy (as in the Ni^{2+} ion) with the odd one in the $d_{x^2-y^2}$-orbital:

(IX)   (X)

Arrangement of nine electrons in the $3d$-orbitals of the Cu^{2+} ion in octahedral (IX) and square-planar (X) ligand-field

The difference between the repulsive forces along the one axis compared with the other two is less than in the d^8-ions of nickel, palladium, platinum and gold, but we can expect a few examples of the truly planar configuration: this is observed in cupric oxide[26], which has a similar structure to palladium oxide (p. 46) and in the vapour of cupric acetylacetonate, which consists of single planar molecules[27]; it also occurs, of course, in the phthalocyanin (XII). One interesting distinction from nickel is that even with ligands producing the lowest ligand-field a truly octahedral environment cannot be expected, and even in cupric fluoride elongated octahedral co-ordination is observed, as it is in the fluorides of the d^4-ions, Cr^{2+} and Mn^{3+} [28].

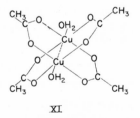

XI

Amongst the compounds of divalent copper, one of the most remarkable structures observed is that of the acetate[29]. This has been found to crystallize in dimeric molecules, $[Cu_2(OCOCH_3)_4.(OH_2)_2]^0$, with a wheel-like shape, the axle formed of a line H_2O—Cu—Cu—OH_2 and the hub of four radially-arranged acetate ions, each linking the two copper ions (XI); the environment of each of the copper atoms is thus: four oxygen atoms in the form of a square at 1·97 Å, one water molecule normal to the plane of this square and at an elongated distance (Cu—O, 2·20 Å) and another copper atom opposite the water molecule at a distance of 2·64 Å, almost identical with that (2·56 Å) observed in metallic copper.

The chromous ion resembles the cupric ion in having an odd number of d_γ-electrons (in this case, one only) over a spherically symmetrical d_ε-group (in this case, half filled only) and chromous acetate is isomorphous with the cupric salt. The close proximity of the Cu^{2+} ions in the cupric acetate molecule results in partial quenching of the paramagnetism, the moment being reduced to about $1·4\beta$ per copper atom. The same low moment is observed in the higher homologues[30] and the dimeric structure is preserved in solutions in non-polar solvents, where the water molecules may be replaced by other donors, such as pyridine, dioxane or the alkanoic acids themselves[31].

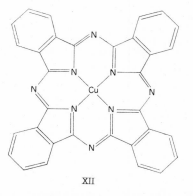

XII

The stereochemistry of divalent silver would be expected to resemble that of cupric copper. The only stable compounds of divalent silver are the orange paramagnetic complexes of nitrogenous bases, such as the pyridine complex, $[Ag(py)_4](S_2O_8)$; the picolinate has been shown to be isomorphous with the corresponding copper complex[32].

REFERENCES

1. L. PAULING, *The Nature of the Chemical Bond.* Cornell University Press, New York (1942).
2. R. S. NYHOLM and R. J. GILLESPIE, *Quart. Rev.* **11**, 339 (1957).
3. N. V. SIDGWICK and H. M. POWELL, *Proc. Roy. Soc.* A **176**, 153 (1940).
4. J. W. LINNETT and C. E. MELLISH, *Trans. Faraday Soc.* **50**, 657 (1954).
5. R. S. NYHOLM, *Quart. Rev.* **7**, 377 (1953); *J. Inorg. Nucl. Chem.* **8**, 401 (1958).
6. D. P. GRADDON, *J. Inorg. Nucl. Chem.* **3**, 308 (1956).
7. H. TAUBE, *Chem. Rev.* **50**, 69 (1952).
8. J. S. GRIFFITH and L. E. ORGEL, *Quart. Rev.* **11**, 381 (1957).
9. N. S. GILL, R. S. NYHOLM and P. PAULING, *Nature, Lond.* **182**, 168 (1958).
10. G. N. TISCHENKO and Z. G. PINSKER, *Dokl. Akad. Nauk S.S.S.R.* **100**, 913 (1955).
11. H. M. POWELL and A. F. WELLS, *J. Chem. Soc.* 359 (1935).
11a. E. FERRONI and E. BONDI, *J. Inorg. Nucl. Chem.* **8**, 458 (1958).

12. H. BRASSEUR, A. DE RASSENFOSSE and J. PIERARD, *Z. Krist.* A **88**, 210 (1934).
13. E. G. COX, F. W. PINKARD, W. WARDLAW and K. C. WEBSTER, *J. Chem. Soc.* 459 (1935).
14. R. W. G. WYCKOFF, *J. Amer. Chem. Soc.* **44**, 1239, 1260 (1922).
15. A. FERRARI and R. CURTI, *Gaz. Chim. Ital.* **63**, 499 (1933).
16. G. T. MORGAN and F. H. BURSTALL, *J. Chem. Soc.* 2213 (1931).
17. C. M. HARRIS, R. S. NYHOLM and N. C. STEVENSON, *Nature, Lond.* **177**, 1127 (1956).
18. N. ELLIOTT and L. PAULING, *J. Amer. Chem. Soc.* **60**, 1846 (1938).
19. R. S. NYHOLM, *Chem. Rev.* **53**, 278 (1953).
20. G. J. BULLEN, *Nature, Lond.* **177**, 537 (1956).
21. L. M. VENANZI, *J. Inorg. Nucl. Chem.* **8**, 137 (1958).
22. J. H. RAYNER and H. M. POWELL, *J. Chem. Soc.* 319 (1952).
23. C. A. BEEVERS and H. S. LIPSON, *Proc. Roy. Soc.* A **146**, 570 (1934).
24. D. HARKER, *Z. Krist.* **93**, 136 (1936).
25. L. HELMHOLZ, *J. Amer. Chem. Soc.* **69**, 886 (1947).
26. G. TUNNELL, E. POSNJAK and C. J. KSANDA, *Z. Krist.* **90**, 120 (1935).
27. S. SHIBATA and K. SONE, *Bull. Chem. Soc. Japan* **29**, 852 (1956).
28. M. A. HEPWORTH, K. H. JACK and R. S. NYHOLM, *Nature, Lond.* **179**, 211 (1957).
29. J. N. VAN NIEKERK and F. R. L. SCHOENING, *Nature, Lond.* **171**, 36 (1953).
30. R. L. MARTIN and H. WATERMAN, *J. Chem. Soc.* 2545 (1957).
31. D. P. GRADDON, *Nature, Lond.* **186**, 715 (1960).
32. E. G. COX, W. WARDLAW and K. C. WEBSTER, *J. Chem. Soc.* 775 (1936).

CHAPTER III

POLYMERIZATION AND CO-ORDINATE SATURATION

THE co-ordination number of an ion is determined by a combination of electronic and steric effects, as a result of which each ion is commonly associated with a particular co-ordination number. The fundamental importance of this co-ordination number is shown by the extent to which it may come to dominate the chemistry of the ion concerned. Thus in many instances when an ion appears, from the empirical formulae of its compounds, to have a co-ordination number less than usual, it is found that polymerization has occurred so as to preserve the usual co-ordination number.

PRESERVATION OF TETRAHEDRAL CO-ORDINATION

A familiar example of the preservation of co-ordination number by polymerization occurs in the aluminium halides. In these the tetrahedral environment of the aluminium atoms is preserved by the formation of dimers, one of the non-bonding pairs of electrons on a halogen atom of one $AlCl_3$ molecule being donated to the aluminium atom of the other (I):

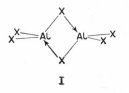

I

The Al—X bonds within the bridge are all equal but longer than the terminal Al—X bonds[1]; this difference in bond lengths decreases with increasing polarizability of the halogen atom. On heating, the dimers dissociate reversibly at 400–600°C the monomeric molecules being plane-triangular:

| Halogen | Length of Al—X bond | |
	bridge	terminal
chloride	2·21	2·06
bromide	2·33	2·21
iodide	2·58	2·53

The fluoride does not dimerize (the fluoride ion is apparently not able to act as a double donor) and the chloride is ionic in the solid state, though dimeric in the vapour at 180–400°C; the bromide and iodide retain the dimeric molecular structures even in the solid state.

The dialkyl aluminium halides, R_2AlX, and the corresponding alkoxides, R_2AlOR, are also dimeric in solution and in the vapour state and the trialkoxides are polymeric, $[Al(OR)_3]_n$. Similar compounds of boron, such as the dialkyl borinates, R_2BOR, are also dimeric, as are the dialkyl alkoxides, sulphides and amines of gallium, R_2GaOR, R_2GaSR and R_2GaNR_2, produced by thermal decomposition of the addition compounds of the dialkylmethylgallium with alcohols, mercaptans or amines, with elimination of methane[2]:

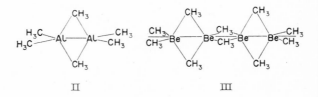

One of the most striking examples of dimerization is that of the aluminium dialkyls, AlR_3, in which the tetrahedral environment of the aluminium atoms is maintained, despite the electron-deficient nature of the dimers produced. The trimethyl, $Al_2(CH_3)_6$, has been shown by X-ray analysis to have a bridged structure (II), in which the Al—C bonds in the bridge are longer (2·24 Å) than the terminal Al—C bonds (2·00 Å) and the Al—Al distance (2·55 Å) corresponds almost exactly to the theoretical distance for an Al—Al single bond[3].

The alkyls of boron show no tendency to dimerize, unless there is at least one hydrogen atom attached to the boron atom, when electron-deficient dimers are produced in which the hydrogen atom is responsible for the bridging; trialkyls of gallium and indium are monomeric in the vapour state, though those of gallium are somewhat associated in solution. Beryllium, however, like aluminium, forms alkyls which are polymerized: the dimethyl, $Be(CH_3)_2$, for instance, which is a solid subliming at 217°C, has been shown by X-ray analysis[4] to have a chain structure in which the tetrahedral environment of the beryllium atoms is maintained in an electron-deficient system (III). The nature of the bonding in the beryllium and aluminium alkyls is now explained in terms of "three-centred bonds", produced by the overlapping of sp^3-hybrid-bond orbitals on the carbon atoms in the bridge with the sp^3-orbitals on each of the aluminium or beryllium atoms (IIIa):

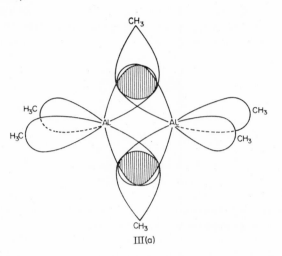

III(a)

Another example of the maintenance of the tetrahedral environment of a beryllium atom is found in the basic acetate, $Be_4O(OCOCH_3)_6$, a solid melting at 285°C, volatile above 330°C and monomeric in the vapour state;

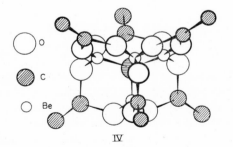

IV

soluble and monomeric in many organic solvents, insoluble in water and hydrolyzed by it on heating. This molecule has been shown by X-ray analysis to be based on a tetrahedral arrangement of four beryllium atoms round a central oxygen atom, each edge of the resulting tetrahedron being completed by co-ordination of acetate ions through both oxygen atoms (IV), so that the tetrahedral co-ordination of each beryllium atom is also preserved [5]. Various homologous compounds are known, derived from other simple carboxylic acids.

The d^{10}-ions of the B sub-group metals (ions of group valency) have similar electronic structures to those of the short period elements and zinc, like beryllium, forms a basic acetate, $Zn_4O(OCOCH_3)_6$, of similar structure to the beryllium compound. Cadmium and mercury also form a number of compounds in which the tetrahedral co-ordination of the metal atom is maintained by dimerization, such as the trialkylphosphine complexes of cadmium and mercuric halides (V) [6].

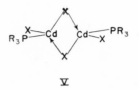

V

The structures of zinc and cadmium cyanides also show this tendency, the cyanide ions acting as double donor groups and so forming linear M—C≡N—M links throughout the crystal, which thus becomes a giant three-dimensional co-ordinated system [7], the carbon and nitrogen atoms being arranged in a random manner within the links (VI):

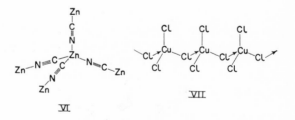

VI   VII

The cuprous halides and silver iodide also have structures in which the metal ions are surrounded tetrahedrally by halide ions (zinc blende structures), despite the comparatively large size of the metal ions (the cuprous ion has almost exactly the same radius as the sodium ion and the silver ion is, of course, larger), which would readily allow the ionic rock salt structure, which is in fact adopted by silver bromide and chloride. It appears therefore that we should regard these cuprous halides and silver iodide as three-dimensional co-ordination systems. This idea is supported by the crystal structure of the double alkali metal cuprous chlorides [8], M_2CuCl_3, in which the $CuCl_3^{2-}$ anions form chain polymers, the cuprous ion being tetrahedrally surrounded by chloride ions (VII). The tetrahedral environment of the copper atoms is also preserved in chalcopyrite (copper pyrites), $CuFeS_2$, which has a wurtzite structure with alternate copper and iron atoms[9], clear evidence that the substance is cuprous ferric sulphide and not cupric ferrous.

One of the most remarkable examples of the preservation of a tetrahedral environment for cuprous and argentous ions occurs in the triethylarsine complexes of the metal iodides, $MI.As(C_2H_5)_3$, which are tetrameric, with the copper or silver and iodine atoms forming a "box" of distorted cubic shape (VIII)[10]. The curious tetrameric thallous alkoxides[11] probably have somewhat similar structures (IX). One interesting feature of these

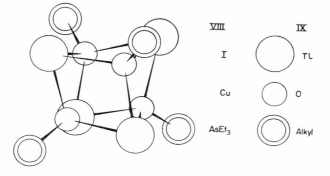

VIII   IX

I   Tl

Cu   O

AsEt₃   Alkyl

Box like molecule of $[CuI.As(C_2H_5)_3]_4$ (VIII) or $[Tl..OAlk]_4$ (IX)

box-like tetrameric structures is that the tetrahedral co-ordination of the Cu^+, Ag^+ or oxygen atoms imposes bond angles considerably less than $90°$ at the iodine or thallium atoms, suggesting that these atoms may be forming hybrid-bond orbitals without the participation of the s-orbitals — an unusual example of the "inert pair" effect.

POLYMERS WITH LINEAR CO-ORDINATION OF THE METAL ION

The larger d^{10}-ions of silver, gold and mercury generally prefer a co-ordination number of two, the 2:co-ordinated groups forming a linear arrangement with the central metal atom as in the silver ammine, $[Ag(NH_3)_2]^+$ and aurocyanide, $[Au(CN)_2]^-$ ions and molecules of the mercuric halides or mercury–organic compounds. This preference is shown in the structures of silver and cuprous oxides[12], each oxide ion being tetra-hedrally co-ordinated to four metal ions and each metal ion linearly to two oxide ions, so that the overall pattern is of oxygen atoms arranged tetrahedrally about one another with cuprous or silver ions in the middle of the O—M—O links in rather the same way as the CN^- ions are placed in zinc cyanide. When the linearly co-ordinated metal ions are combined with doubly co-ordinating anions, the result is the formation of a chain structure; in silver cyanide[13] the chains are straight due to the linear disposition of the co-ordinating bonds of the cyanide ions (X) but in the thiocyanate[14] a zig-zag chain is produced due to the bond angle at the sulphur atoms (XI):

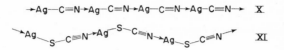

Zig-zag chains also occur in aurous iodide[15], and in mercuric oxide[16] the dihedral angle at the oxygen atoms leads to a spiral arrangement of the chains.

THE PRESERVATION OF SQUARE-PLANAR CO-ORDINATION

Whereas univalent gold has a d^{10}-ion with tetrahedral or linear co-ordination, trivalent gold belongs to the small group of d^8-ions for which square-planar co-ordination is normal. This group also includes divalent platinum, palladium and nickel, the stereochemistry of the latter having already been discussed in detail.

The auric halides, AuX_3, have been shown to be dimeric in non-donor solvents, though monomeric in donor solvents such as pyridine, which evidently co-ordinate in the fourth position. X-ray analysis of the chloride[17] has shown that the dimers have a bridged structure with all the atoms in one plane and Au—Cl bonds longer in the bridge (2·33 Å) than in the terminal bonds (2·24 Å) (XII):

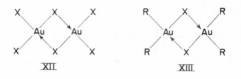

Treatment of the pyridine solutions of auric halides with Grignard reagents gives alkyl derivatives, but the trialkyls cannot be isolated from solution (owing to the difficulty of maintaining the co-ordination number); the dialkyl halides are shown to be dimeric in non-donor solvents (XIII) and on treatment with silver sulphate give corresponding sulphates $(R_2Au)_2SO_4$, which are, rather surprisingly, also dimeric. With silver cyanide, the dialkyl gold cyanides, R_2AuCN, are formed; these are found to be tetrameric in solution[18] and the structure (XIV), based on the combination of the square planar co-ordination of the gold atoms with the linear bond distribution of the cyanide groups, has been confirmed by X-ray analysis[19]. All of the atoms lie in the same plane.

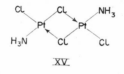

XIV.

Numerous examples are known of the preservation of the square-planar co-ordination of divalent palladium and platinum by dimerization, and a single example is sufficient to establish the principle. The ammine dichloride of platinum was shown to be dimeric and used by Werner in support of his proposal of the general adoption of the square-planar configuration in platinous complexes (XV):

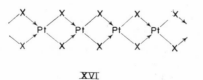

XV

Polymerized systems based on square-planar co-ordination about palladous or platinous ions occur in the MX_2 halides (XVI). In the solid halides chain molecules of this type are packed lying parallel to one another[20], but with the ribbons tilted relative to each other so that the only atoms within bonding distance of the platinum or palladium atoms are those of its own chain, that is these chain molecules are packed in the crystal as if they were organic

XVI

in type (for diagram and comparison with cupric chloride see p. 35). Chains of this type also occur in the corresponding oxides, PdO and PtO[21] and sulphides, PdS and PtS but in these the chains are so arranged that in addition to the square-planar co-ordination of the metal being preserved, the oxygen or sulphur atoms also retain their normal symmetry by tetrahedral co-ordination to four metal atoms (XVII). Cupric oxide is similar, as is the oxide of divalent silver, AgO[22]:

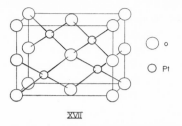

XVII

OCTAHEDRALLY CO-ORDINATED POLYMERS

Numerous examples of polymerized and bridged structures are known amongst the octahedral co-ordination compounds of the Pt^{4+}, Co^{3+}, Cr^{3+} and other ions, the co-ordination number being preserved by single, double or even triple bridges. A good example of the double-bridged type is the octammino-μ-dioxycobaltic sulphate (XVIII) formed by the action of heat on the sulphate of the aquopentamminocobaltic ion.

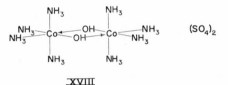

XVIII

The alkoxides of many A sub-group metals have also been found to be polymeric in solution; this polymerization has been explained by the need to maintain octahedral co-ordination. Thus the alkoxides of columbium and tantalum are dimeric (XIX), whereas those of titanium and zirconium are trimeric (XX). Association observed in the hexalkoxides of uranium suggest that with the very largest metals co-ordinate saturation requires the maintenance of even higher co-ordination numbers[23].

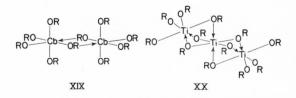

XIX   XX

Combination of octahedrally co-ordinated metal ions with the linear bond distribution of the cyanide ion leads to the formation of giant three-dimensional co-ordinated systems such as that of ferric cyanide[24], in which the arrangement of the cyanide ions is probably random throughout the entire crystal (XXI). This substance, which is obtained by precipitation of potassium ferricyanide with a ferric salt, is used as a pigment under the name "Berlin green". Precipitation of potassium ferricyanide with a ferrous salt or of potassium ferrocyanide with a ferric salt produces blue pigments, known respectively as Turnbull's blue and Prussian blue. Apart from differing degrees of hydration and variations in particle size and shade of colour, depending on precipitation conditions, these two substances have been shown to be identical; the empirical formula, $KFe_2(CN)_6$, is obtained by the replacement of half of the ferric ions in the ferric cyanide structure by ferrous ions (apparently with a random distribution of the two valency states) and the inclusion of sufficient potassium ions to maintain electrical neutrality; these potassium ions are located at the centres of alternate cubes in the structure (XXIa).

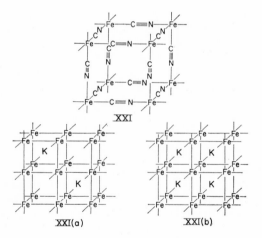

The nearly white precipitate, $KFe(CN)_3$, obtained from potassium ferrocyanide and a ferrous salt, also has the same fundamental structure, with all of the iron atoms in the ferrous state and the electrical neutrality maintained by the presence of a potassium ion at the centre of each cube throughout the structure (XXIb).

Similar structures have been observed in some more complicated insoluble complex cyanides such as the potassium–copper–iron cyanides and are probably a general feature of complex cyanide chemistry.

One of the most remarkable examples of the preservation of octahedral co-ordination occurs in the platinum alkyls. Platinic chloride reacts with Grignard reagents to form trialkyl halides such as $Pt(CH_3)_3I$; with sodium methyl these give tetramethyl platinum, $Pt(CH_3)_4$. Both are comparatively stable solids, soluble in organic solvents, and tetrameric in solution. They are insoluble in water. The structures of these tetramers have been determined by X-ray analysis[25]: both have the same type of molecule, based on a distorted cube of four platinum atoms and four halogen or carbon atoms (XXII, XXIII):

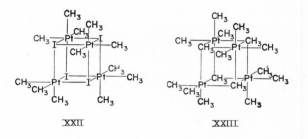

The trialkyl halides achieve octahedral co-ordination of the platinum atoms by bridging with triply-donating halogen atoms (compare the tetrameric trialkylarsine cuprous iodide, VIII); in platinum tetramethyl the bridging is by methyl groups, the molecule being electron deficient and presumably involving four-centre bonds (compare the alkyls of aluminium and beryllium, II and III).

On treatment of a benzene solution of trimethyl platinum iodide with powdered platinum, hexamethyl platinum, $Pt_2(CH_3)_6$, is obtained, monomeric in organic solvents, structure unknown.

REFERENCES

1. K. J. PALMER and N. ELLIOTT, *J. Amer. Chem. Soc.* **60**, 1852 (1938).
2. G. E. COATES, *Organo-metallic Compounds* pp. 84–94. Methuen, London (1956).
3. P. H. LEWIS and R. E. RUNDLE, *J. Chem. Phys.* **21**, 986 (1953).
4. A. I. SNOW and R. E. RUNDLE, *Acta Cryst.* **4**, 348 (1951).
5. L. PAULING and J. SHERMAN, *Proc. Nat. Acad. Sci., Wash.* **20**, 340 (1934).
6. F. G. MANN, D. PURDIE, R. C. EVANS and H. S. PEISER, *J. Chem. Soc.* 1209, 1230 (1940).
7. G. S. ZHDANOV, *Dokl. Akad. Nauk S.S.S.R.* **31**, 352 (1941).
8. C. BRINK and C. H. MACGILLAVRY, *Acta Cryst.* **2**, 158 (1949).
9. A. F. WELLS, *Structural Inorganic Chemistry*, (2nd Ed.), pp. 402–403. Oxford University Press (1950).
10. A. F. WELLS, *Z. Krist.* **94**, 447 (1936).
11. N. V. SIDGWICK and L. E. SUTTON, *J. Chem. Soc.* 1461 (1930).
12. P. NIGGLI, *Z. Krist.* **57**, 253 (1922).
13. C. D. WEST, *Z. Krist.* **90**, 555 (1935).
14. I. LINDQVIST, *Acta Cryst.* **10**, 29 (1957).
15. A. WEISS and A. WEISS, *Z. Natürf.* **11b**, 604 (1956).
16. K. AURIVILLIUS and I. B. CARLSSON, *Acta Chem. Scand.* **11**, 1069 (1957).

17. CLARK, Thesis, University of California, in *Ann. Rep. Progr. Chem.* (1955).
18. A. BURAWOY, C. S. GIBSON and S. HOLT, *J. Chem. Soc.* 1024 (1935).
19. R. F. PHILLIPS and H. M. POWELL, *Proc. Roy. Soc.* A **173**, 147 (1939).
20. A. F. WELLS, *Z. Krist.* **100**, 189 (1938).
21. W. J. MOORE and L. PAULING, *J. Amer. Chem. Soc.* **63**, 1392 (1941).
22. V. SCATTURIN, P. L. BELLON and R. ZANNETTI, *J. Inorg. Nucl. Chem.* **8**, 462 (1958).
23. D. C. BRADLEY, *Nature, Lond.* **182**, 1211 (1958).
24. J. F. KEGGIN and F. D. MILES, *Nature, Lond.* **137**, 577 (1936).
25. R. E. RUNDLE and J. H. STURDIVANT, *J. Amer. Chem. Soc.* **69**, 1561 (1947).

E

CHAPTER IV

THE STABILITY OF COMPLEX SALTS

COMPLEX compounds are often described qualitatively as "stable" or "unstable"; the cobaltammines, for example, and many of the complex cyanides are obviously stable in the sense that they can be kept indefinitely without decomposition and, in solution, fail to give the normal analytical reactions of their constituents. Other compounds, like many of the hydrocarbon and carbonyl complexes, are very readily decomposed by heat or hydrolysed by water or are photosensitive.

In this chapter we shall not be primarily concerned with stability in this sense, but with the numerous co-ordination compounds of metal cations which, to a greater or lesser extent, undergo reactions in which one ligand replaces another reversibly. In particular, the most familiar example of this behaviour is the reaction of complex salts with a solvent (nearly always water) to form the solvated (hydrated) metal ion and free ligands:

$$ML_n + nH_2O \rightleftharpoons M(OH_2)_n + nL\dagger$$

The reverse of this reaction represents the formation of a complex ion from its constituents in aqueous solution and must proceed by a stepwise replacement of co-ordinated water molecules by ligand molecules or ions:

$$M(OH_2)_n + L \rightleftharpoons M(OH_2)_{n-1}L + OH_2$$
$$M(OH_2)_{n-1}L + L \rightleftharpoons M(OH_2)_{n-2}L_2 + OH_2 \ldots$$
$$\ldots M(OH_2)L_{n-1} + L \rightleftharpoons ML_n + OH_2$$

For each step in this process there is an equilibrium constant defined by the expressions:

$$k_1 = \frac{[M(OH_2)_{n-1}L]}{[M(OH_2)_n] \times [L]}$$

$$k_2 = \frac{[M(OH_2)_{n-2}L_2]}{[M(OH_2)_{n-1}L] \times [L]} \quad \ldots$$

$$\ldots k_n = \frac{[ML_n]}{[M(OH_2)L_{n-1}] \times [L]}$$

The constants $k_1, k_2, \ldots k_n$ are the successive stability constants of the system. For statistical reasons and because of the repulsion of a co-ordinated

---

† Throughout this chapter the charges on the metal atoms and the ligands are omitted in general equations so as to avoid confusion.

ligand for an incoming ligand of similar type the values of these constants nearly always decrease in the order

$$k_1 > k_2 > k_3 > \ldots \ldots k_n$$

as in the examples in Table 1.

TABLE 1. SUCCESSIVE AND OVERALL STABILITY CONSTANTS $(\log k_n)$[1]

System	$\log k_1$	$\log k_2$	$\log k_3$	$\log k_4$	$\log k_5$	$\log k_6$	$\log \beta$
Cu^{2+}/NH_3	4·15	3·50	2·89	2·13	−0·52		12·7 (β_4)
Ni^{2+}/NH_3	2·80	2·24	1·73	1·19	0·75	0·03	8·7
Cd^{2+}/I^-	2·08	0·77	2·15	1·48			6·5
Cr^{3+}/SCN^-	3·1	1·7	1·0	0·3	−0·7	−1·6	3·8

The product of the successive stability constants:

$$k_1 \times k_2 \times k_3 \ldots \ldots \times k_n = \frac{[ML_n]}{[M(OH_2)_n] \times [L]^n} = \beta$$

is the overall stability constant of the system and is commonly used as a general guide to the stability of the complex in this sense.

Values of the overall stability constant may cover a very wide range: for extremely stable complexes, such as the ferrocyanide ion, $[Fe(CN)_6]^{4-}$, values greater than 10^{30} may occur and for very unstable complexes β may even be less than unity; on account of this wide range the values of the constants are frequently quoted on a logarithmic scale:

$$pk = \log_{10} k$$

As a rough guide, a $p\beta$ value greater than about 8 represents what we should normally think of as a "stable" complex.

THE DETERMINATION OF STABILITY CONSTANTS

In principle stability constants are determined by studying the concentrations of the various species present in a wide range of equilibrium mixtures containing the metal ion and the ligand in different proportions. For a reasonably stable complex the dominant species present with a given ligand–metal ratio are those with the nearest integral ratios above and below; for example, for a ligand–metal ratio of 2·7 : 1, the species predominantly present are ML_2 and ML_3. It is thus possible, by adjusting the ligand–metal ratio to examine experimentally successive steps in the process of complex formation.

First, however, it is necessary to establish the number of steps in the equilibrium, that is the maximum number of ligands which can be attached to each metal atom. This is not necessarily the same as the co-ordination number or the number of ligands attached to the metal in any solid compound which may be isolated, as in solution some of the ligands may be displaced by the solvent, particularly if this is water.

The stoichiometry of the system under the conditions of the experiment is determined by Job's method of continuous variations: some property is chosen which changes as complex formation takes place (for example, colour intensity, pH or an electrode potential) and plotted as ordinate against the concentrations of the metal cation and the ligand put into solution, the sum of these concentrations being kept constant. If no complex formation occurs the result will be a straight line (Fig. 1), but if complex formation occurs a curve will be obtained (Fig. 2); the difference between this curve and the straight line of Fig. 1 is then plotted and will be found to represent two intersecting straight lines (or, if the complexes formed are of low stability, it may become rounded) (Fig. 3); the ligand–metal ratio represented by the point of intersection is the ratio in the highest complex formed in solution and hence also the number of steps in the process.

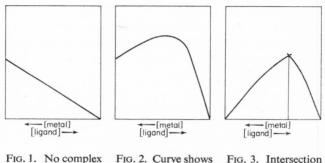

FIG. 1. No complex   FIG. 2. Curve shows   FIG. 3. Intersection
       formation   complex formation   shows 2 : 1 complex

The first step in complex formation may now be examined by investigating the variation of a suitable physical property over an appropriate range of concentrations of metal and ligand (but the value of this property representing completion of the first step in complex formation will have to be found by trial and error as it will not correspond exactly to the value observed for a 1 : 1 ratio).

In order to overcome the difficulties introduced by variations in the ionic strength of the medium, it is usual to carry out these experiments at an arbitrary ionic strength, controlled by the addition of a non-complexing electrolyte, such as sodium perchlorate. Thermodynamic equilibrium constants may then be obtained by application of the Debye–Hückel theory or of one of the approximation formulae derived from it; such formulae are, however, not applicable at ionic strengths greater than about 0·1. Furthermore the theory is based on the consideration of ions as point charges and many of the ligands used in co-ordination chemistry are of considerable size, so that the only really reliable method for obtaining thermodynamic equilibrium constants is that in which the whole of the measurements are repeated at a series of different ionic strengths and the thermodynamic constants obtained by extrapolation to zero ionic strength.

Though simple in principle, the determination of a whole series of thermodynamic equilibrium constants is, in practice, exceedingly difficult and involves considerable mathematical manipulation. This mathematical treatment will not be discussed here; it is readily available in some detail in Martell and Calvin's recently published book[2]. There is also an excellent introduction, giving copious references to the original literature, in the monograph published by the Chemical Society[3].

Whilst almost every known physical method of investigating solutions has been applied to the study of complexing equilibria, the most widely used methods fall into two classes:

1. *Optical Methods*

These are usually spectrophotometric and depend on the difference in the colour or absorption spectra of the "free" and complexed ions, either the ligand or the metal being the coloured species, or in some cases the complex formed, which may be much more highly coloured than either of the other species.

Let us suppose that at a selected wavelength the optical density of an aqueous solution of a transition metal salt is three units and that we are examining the first step in complex formation; the optical density of the solution containing a 1 : 1 ratio of ligand to metal is found to be, say, twelve units; if formation of the 1 : 1 complex, ML, is complete under these conditions then an optical density of twelve units corresponds to the colour of this complex, but it is more likely that a small excess of the ligand will have to be added to complete this step in complex formation, so that the optical density of the 1 : 1 complex is really a little higher, perhaps thirteen units; let us guess that this is the right figure.

There are now ten units difference in optical density between the solution of the metal ion and the solution of the complex ML, so that the proportion of "free" and complexed metal ion in any solution of intermediate optical density can be estimated by simple proportion: a solution of optical density ten units, for example, would have seven-tenths of the metal in the complexed form. If then we determine the optical densities of a number of solutions containing various proportions of metal and ligand, we can find the proportion of the metal in the complexed form in each solution; since we know the initial concentrations of the metal and the ligand we can thus calculate the concentration of the complex ML and, by difference, of the "free" metal and ligand and hence obtain the equilibrium constant:

$$k_1 = \frac{[ML]}{[M] \times [L]}$$

If our guess at the optical density of the complex ML is correct the values of k_1 obtained for all the solutions of intermediate optical density will be the same; if the values of k_1 drift upwards or downwards as the ligand–metal ratio changes, this shows that our guess at the optical density of the ML complex was not quite right, so we have to guess again and recalculate the values of k_1; this process is repeated until there is no drift, when the scatter of the values of k_1 gives an idea of the accuracy of the result.

Spectrophotometric methods of measuring colour intensity are of only limited accuracy (about ± 1 per cent) and as the concentrations of some of the species are obtained by difference this means that this method cannot be used for reactions which are heavily one-sided; if, for instance, complex formation was always at least 99 per cent complete, the optical densities observed would be indistinguishable from those which would be observed if complex formation were 100 per cent complete. The spectrophotometric method is, however, particularly suitable for the study of less-stable complexes, where complex formation approaches completeness only in the presence of a considerable excess of the ligand.

2. *Electrochemical Methods*

Exactly the same principles are applied where an electrochemical method is used as have been described for the spectrophotometric method. The simplest of the electrochemical methods is that in which the concentration of "free" metal is determined in an equilibrium of the type:

$$M + nL \rightleftharpoons ML_n$$

The total concentrations of the metal cation and the ligand are either known or determined by standard analytical methods; the concentration of the "free" metal is determined potentiometrically or polarographically and that of the complexed metal by difference.

Another widely-used electrochemical method is that in which the pH of the solution is determined in a competition reaction of the type:

$$M^{m+} + nLH \rightleftharpoons ML_n^{(m-n)+} + nH^+$$

This method can only be applied where the ligand, L, is the anion of a weak acid, so that its co-ordination to the metal atom is accompanied by the release of hydrogen ions; it could not be applied satisfactorily, for example, to the co-ordination of chloride ions, since the conjugate acid of the ligand would be a strong acid and already fully ionized before complex formation took place.

Electrochemical methods have the advantage over spectrophotometric methods of greater sensitivity, but are not suitable for use in any but the most dilute solutions. For the most stable complexes even electrochemical methods are not sufficiently sensitive to allow the determination of the successive complexing constants, but there is some prospect that radio chemical methods may prove suitable. In these cases the overall stability constant can be obtained from the effect of complex formation on the standard electrode potential of the metal:

$$\ln \beta = \frac{nF}{RT} \left\{ E^{\circ}_{\text{aqueous}} - E^{\circ}_{\text{complex}} \right\}$$

FACTORS AFFECTING STABILITY CONSTANTS[4]

Stability constants vary over a very wide range of values even when we consider only the reaction of a single ligand with a number of metals or a single metal with a variety of ligands. It is thus not possible, as a general rule, to say that any particular metal or any particular ligand forms complexes of outstandingly high or low stability. It is therefore apparent that no single factor can be expected to account for the stabilities of complex salts, but that each case must be considered separately in terms of a subtle blend of contributing factors.

The Electrostatic Factor

Since complex formation is essentially a reaction between a cation and an anion or dipole, the ionic potential (charge–radius ratio) of the cation can be expected to be of paramount importance. It is for this reason that, when a metal forms complexes with the same ligand in more than one valency state, the complexes of the higher valency are nearly always more stable. Table 2 gives some examples of the stability constants of EDTA complexes with metals in two different valency states.

TABLE 2. EFFECT OF VALENCY ON STABILITY OF EDTA COMPLEXES

Cation	V^{2+}	Fe^{2+}	Co^{2+}	Eu^{2+}
pk	12·7	14·3	16·2	7·7
Cation	V^{3+}	Fe^{3+}	Co^{3+}	Eu^{3+}
pk	25·9	25·1	36	17·3

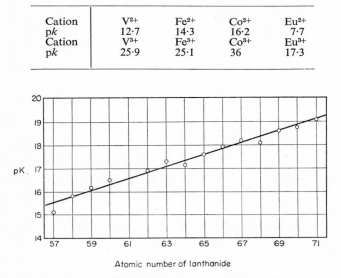

Atomic number of lanthanide

FIG. 4. Stability constants of lanthanide–EDTA complexes

The ionic potential effect is particularly well illustrated by the regular rise in stability of the lanthanide–EDTA complexes from lanthanum to lutecium due to the "lanthanide contraction", which leads to a steady increase in ionic potential with increasing atomic number (Fig. 4).

Somewhat similar results are observed for complexes of the divalent ions of the transition metals of the first long period. IRVING and WILLIAMS[5] have shown that the same order of increasing stability:

$$Mn < Fe < Co < Ni < Cu > Zn$$

holds, irrespective of the nature of the ligand (Fig. 2) and this is also the order of decreasing ionic radius (Cu^{2+} smallest). Similar orders had been previously observed by various authors[6, 7], who also included other, non-transitional ions in their series; but the order in which these "outside" ions appear differs from one ligand to another.

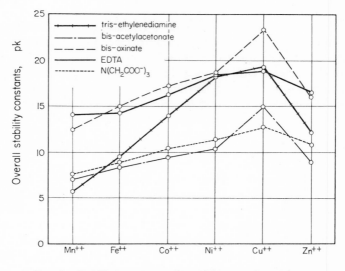

FIG. 5.   Stability constants of transition-metal complexes

The failure of cations outside the transition metal series to fit into these stability orders always in the same positions, clearly indicates that other factors are involved besides the electrostatic attraction between the cations and the ligands. Probably the most important of these is the need to maintain a correct balance of electrical charge in every part of the complex.

The Principle of Charge Distribution

The process of co-ordination involves the "donation" of a pair of electrons from each ligand to the metal cation. If the bond formed were a perfect covalent bond this would result in the effective transfer of one unit of charge to the metal atom for each co-ordinate bond formed. For a 6:co-ordinate divalent cation this would lead to an accumulation of four negative charges on the metal atom. Such a system would clearly be unstable and it is evident that in stable systems the co-ordinate bonds must have considerable polarity.

The extent of electron transfer in any one case depends upon two factors: (a) the ionic potential of the cation; (b) the polarizability of the anion, and as each of these increases so must the amount of negative electrical charge accumulating on the metal atom.

We thus find that stabilities of the complexes of any particular ion increase with increasing polarizability of the ligand, but that there is a limit to this increase because ligands of too high a polarizability would cause the accumulation of too much negative charge on the central atom. For the divalent metal cations from Mn^{2+} to Zn^{2+} stabilities of complexes are found to increase with changing donor atom in the order:

$$F < O < N > S > P$$

donor atoms of the second short period evidently producing too great a transfer of charge to the metal atom.

Such charge transfer may be reduced by a lowering of the co-ordination number as in the ferric-halide complexes where the change of ligand from the fluoride ion to the chloride ion is accompanied by a change from the octahedral $[FeF_6]^{3-}$ to the tetrahedral $[FeCl_4]^-$ ion. A similar change is shown by the Co^{2+} ion and whereas the Ni^{2+} ion forms octahedral complexes with water or amines as ligands, the complexes in which some of the ligands are substituted phosphines are 4:co-ordinated.

It has been suggested that the balance of polarizability of the ligand and ionic potential of the metal cation is ideally such as to produce electrical neutrality on the metal atom and this is probably near the truth for typical transition-metal ions; it cannot, however, be expected for other types of ion; in particular, ions with inert-gas structures may be expected to offer considerable resistance to the transfer of negative electrical charge, the ideal balance in these instances being that which will leave the cation with its positive charge only slightly lowered.

Irving and Williams propose that the ability to accept transferred charge should be related to the gaseous ionization potentials of the cations, since these are a measure of the energy involved in the reverse process:

$$M_{(gas)} - n\bar{e} = M^{n+}_{(gas)}$$

In practice, however, we are not concerned with gaseous ions but with the behaviour of ions in aqueous solution and a quantity more closely related to the actual processes involved in co-ordination is the standard electrode potential of the metal:

$$M_{(solid)} - n\bar{e} = M^{n+}_{(aqueous)}$$

which is closely related to the ionization potential, but includes terms representing the sublimation energy of the metal and the energy of hydration of the cations.

Table 3 shows the standard electrode potentials of some common metal ions and it can be seen that they fall into three main groups:

(a) Inert gas ions for which $E° <$ about $- 1.5$ V.

(b) Transition metal ions, $E°$ between about 0 and $- 1.0$ V.

(c) Noble metal ions of d^8- or d^{10}-structure, $E° >$ about 0.5 V.

TABLE 3. STANDARD ELECTRODE POTENTIALS OF CATIONS (V)

K^+	$- 2.92$	Ti^{2+}	$- 1.75$	Hg^{2+}	$+ 0.85$
Na^+	$- 2.71$	V^{2+}	$- 1.5$	Cu^+	$+ 0.52$
Ba^{2+}	$- 2.90$	Cr^{2+}	$- 0.86$	Ag^+	$+ 0.80$
Sr^{2+}	$- 2.89$	Mn^{2+}	$- 1.05$	Au^+	$+ 1.68$
Ca^{2+}	$- 2.87$	Fe^{2+}	$- 0.44$	Au^{3+}	$+ 1.4$
Mg^{2+}	$- 2.34$	Co^{2+}	$- 0.28$	Pt^{2+}	$+ 1.2$
Be^{2+}	$- 1.70$	Ni^{2+}	$- 0.25$	Pd^{2+}	$+ 0.83$
La^{2+}	$- 2.37$	Cu^{2+}	$+ 0.35$	Co^{3+}	$+ 0.43$
Al^{3+}	$- 1.67$	Zn^{2+}	$- 0.76$	Fe^{3+}	$- 0.04$
TiO^{2+}	$- 1.0$	Cd^{2+}	$- 0.40$	Cr^{3+}	$- 0.71$

These figures refer to the M/M^{n+} couple, but it must be remembered that there may be intermediate oxidation states.

The first group includes all those cations which form their most stable complexes with fluoride ions or ligands with oxygen as donor atom, for example:

$$[Mg(C_2O_4)_2]^{2-}, \; Be_4O(OOC.CH_3)_6, \; TiF_6^{2-}$$

even nitrogen usually being too good a donor to form stable complexes. In this group in particular the relative stabilities of complexes with different ligands are very sensitive to slight changes in the balance of ionic potential, ionization potential and polarizability, so that no consistent pattern emerges even in so closely related a series of cations as Mg^{2+}, Ca^{2+} and Sr^{2+}.

The second group includes those ions which form complexes of increasing stability as the ligand atom changes in the order:

$$F < O < N > S > P$$

and as nearly all of the complexes of these ions which have been studied have had oxygen or nitrogen as donor atoms a stability order dependent on the ionic potential of the metal is commonly observed (the Irving–Williams order), but we might expect that this order may no longer hold for complexes in which sulphur or phosphorus atoms act as donors.

The third group consists of the heavier ions with d^{10}- or d^8-structures. These are the ions of the "noble" metals, which have considerable positive electrode potentials and consequently a much greater ability to accept transferred negative charge. They thus form their most stable complexes with ligands of highest polarizability, stabilities varying as the donor atom changes in the order:

$$P > S \gg N > O > F \ll Cl < Br < I$$

The ions in this group are also just those which form stable π-complexes with olefins (see Chapter VI) and the abrupt increase in stability of their complexes when the donor atom changes from nitrogen to phosphorus (or arsenic) is taken to indicate that any excessive transfer of charge from the ligand to the metal atom can be relieved by the "back co-ordination" of non-bonding electrons of the metal ion to vacant d-orbitals of the donor atom[8] as is shown to occur in some of the metal carbonyls. In this context it is interesting to note that these metals, whose ions are able to adjust to varying degrees of charge transfer in this way are also those which do not form stable carbonyl-type compounds in the zero-valent state.

The Ligand-field Approach

The stability constants of complexes are related to the free energy changes accompanying their formation and consequently can be divided into a temperature-dependent entropy term and a temperature-independent heat of reaction:

$$- RT \ln K = \Delta G = \Delta H - T\Delta S$$

In order to evaluate both of these terms thermodynamic stability constants must be evaluated over a range of temperatures, and not enough work of this sort has yet been done for a general picture to emerge.

Independent thermochemical values of ΔH are, however, available for some systems and show a similar pattern to the pK values in Fig. 5. These values are shown in Fig. 6 for the hydration of the divalent ions of the first transition series (upper, continuous line) and other systems give similar, double-humped curves, which have been interpreted in terms of ionization potentials, which follow the same pattern.

The lower (broken) line in Fig. 6 represents the same values of ΔH, corrected for the "orbital stabilizing energy" arising from the ligand-field treatment of high-spin complexes. This line shows the regular increase in ΔH with increasing atomic number which would be expected, as the ions contract under the influence of rising nuclear charge (compare the stabilities of the lanthanide–EDTA complexes, Fig. 4).

This "orbital stabilizing energy" arises when successive electrons are placed in the lower energy d_ε-orbitals and is lost when the higher energy d_γ-orbitals are used[9]. The stabilizing energy thus increases from d^1- to d^3-ions, then drops in the d^4- and d^5-ions, after which it rises again from d^6- to d^8-ions and drops to the d^{10}-ion.

Another example of the stabilizing effect of placing electrons in the lower (d_ε) orbitals is provided by the increased stability of complexes which accompanies a change of magnetic susceptibility of an ion. Thus, on grounds of increased electrostatic attraction, all ferric complexes should be more stable than the corresponding ferrous complexes; but in the case of the tris-dipyridyl and tris-o-phenanthroline complexes the ferric compounds are of the high-spin type whereas the ferrous complexes are of the low-spin, dia-magnetic type. The additional stabilization thus provided in the ferrous compounds is sufficient to reverse the usual order of stabilities:

$$[\text{Fe}(o\text{-phen})]^{2+} \quad \text{low spin} \quad \text{p}\beta = 21\cdot3$$
$$[\text{Fe}(o\text{-phen})]^{3+} \quad \text{high-spin} \quad \text{p}\beta = 14\cdot1$$

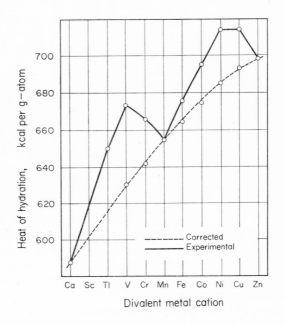

FIG. 6.   Heats of hydration of transition metal cations

Chelation

The stabilities of complexes are greatly increased by the co-ordination of polydentate ligands. The co-ordination of such ligands produces ring structures, the metal atom forming part of the ring; this process is known as chelation (Greek: $\chi\varepsilon\lambda\varepsilon$, a crab's claw).

The most familiar chelating agents are the organic polyamines, poly-carboxylic acids, amino acids and β-diketones. The increased stability due to chelation is readily observed by comparing the co-ordinating power of the oxalate ion with that of the open chain carboxylic acids: carboxylate ions are usually poor ligands forming very unstable complexes; very few complex anions of the type $[\text{M}(\text{OOC.R})_4]^{n-}$ or $[\text{M}(\text{OOC.R})_6]^{n-}$ can be isolated in complex salts, but many metals form stable crystalline complex oxalates with $[\text{M}(\text{C}_2\text{O}_4)_2]^{n-}$ or $[\text{M}(\text{C}_2\text{O}_4)_3]^{n-}$ anions and also corresponding malonates, and those of some transition metals, such as $[Co(C_2O_4)_3]^{3-}$, are highly stable in solution. Table 4 shows the overall stability constants for a number of metal ammines and the corresponding ethylenediamine complexes, the higher stabilities of the latter being apparent in the octahedral and square complexes.

TABLE 4. OVERALL STABILITIES OF AMMINES AND
ETHYLENEDIAMINE COMPLEXES

Cation	Co-ordination No.	$p\beta$ (NH_3)	$p\beta$ (en)
Co^{2+}	6	5	14
Co^{3+}	6	34	49
Ni^{2+}	6	9	19
Cu^{2+}	4 (sq.)	13	20
Zn^{2+}	4 (tet.)	9	11
Cu^{+}	2 (lin.)	11	11
Ag^{+}	2 (lin.)	7	8

Still greater stabilization can be achieved by the use of ligands with larger numbers of co-ordinating groups, such as the anions of nitrilotriacetic acid (I) or ethylenediaminetetra-acetic acid (II), which have four and six donor atoms, respectively, so arranged that all are sterically capable of co-ordination to the same metal cation. The stability of the EDTA complexes is so great that in alkaline solution EDTA will prevent the precipitation of calcium by oxalate or barium by sulphate.

Qualitatively the chelate effect can be explained by comparing the first step in the dissociation of the chelate and open chain type of complexes:

Once an ammonia molecule has been displaced by water it passes into the bulk of the solution and has to compete with the far more numerous water molecules for re-entry, but in the ethylenediamine complex the displaced amino-group is retained in the immediate neighbourhood of the metal atom and is consequently in a favourable position to compete with the solvent.

Quantitatively the chelate effect can be seen to be an entropy effect, attributable to the change in the number of degrees of freedom of the system when a chelate ring is formed:

$$[M(OH_2)_2] + en \rightleftharpoons [M(en)] + 2OH_2$$

two species   three species

and it has been shown that the displacement of ammonia in the complex $[Ni(NH_3)_6]^{2+}$ ion by ethylenediamine to give $[Ni(en)_3]^{2+}$ is accompanied by a large entropy change but only a small heat of reaction.

One factor of great importance in chelation is the size of ring produced; stabilization occurs only when the ring formed is five- or six-membered. This can be seen readily from a comparison of the co-ordinating properties of the anions of the first four dicarboxylic acids:

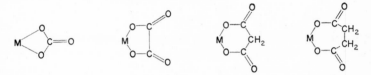

Many metal oxalates and malonates are freely soluble in the presence of excess alkali oxalate or malonate with the formation of complex anions containing five- or six-membered chelate rings, but carbonates and succinates do not dissolve in excess of the alkali metal salts, except at very high concentrations of the alkali metal compounds, the chelate rings which would be formed in the complex anions being four- or seven-membered.

There is not usually much difference in the stabilizing effect of five- or six-membered rings, but one classical experiment should be mentioned which shows the preference for the five-membered structure under conditions of direct competition[10]: 1:2:3-triaminopropane (III) has three ligand atoms but, for steric reasons, can only behave as a bidentate donor; there is thus direct competition between co-ordination by the 1:2-amino groups leading to a five-membered chelate ring and co-ordination by the 1:3-amino groups leading to a six-membered ring. Consequently there are two alternative structures (IV, V) for the neutral complex formed by this compound with platinic chloride:

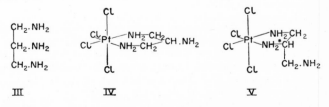

Of these two forms, that with the six-membered ring has no asymmetric carbon atom (IV), whereas that with the five-membered ring (V) has an asymmetric carbon atom and could be resolved into optical isomers, showing the preference for the five-membered ring.

In a few cases abnormal chelate effects are observed as a result of the stereochemistry imposed on the complex by the nature of the metal atom. Silver, for example, fails to form a chelate with ethylenediamine, the normal complex being $[Ag(-NH_2.CH_2.CH_2.NH_2)_2]^+$, and the stability of the 1:1-complexes increases as the number of CH_2 groups in the chain increases[11]. This effect is evidently due to the preference of the Ag^+ ion for linear 2:co-ordination, the longer chains then being those which can form stable chelate rings (VI):

VI

Similarly, the amines (VII) and (VIII) are sterically suited best for tetrahedral and planar 4:co-ordination, respectively:

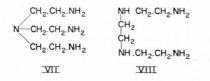

VII   VIII

and this causes a marked change in the relative stabilities of the complexes with Zn^{2+} (normally tetrahedral) and Cu^{2+} (planar):

	Cu^{2+}	Zn^{2+}
pk with (VII) as ligand	18·8	14·6
pk with (VIII) as ligand	20·5	11·8

To here

REFERENCES

1. A. R. Burkin, *Quart. Rev.* **5**, 1 (1951).
2. A. E. Martell and M. Calvin, *Chemistry of the Metal Chelates*, pp. 76–133. Prentice Hall, New York (1952).
3. J. Bjerrum, G. Schwarzenbach and L. C. Sillen, *Stability Constants*. Chemical Society Special Publication (1957).
4. H. M. N. H. Irving, *The Stability of Metal Complexes*. International Conference in Co-ordination Chemistry, Chemical Society Special Publication (1959).
5. H. M. N. H. Irving and R. J. P. Williams, *J. Chem. Soc.* 3192 (1953).
6. D. P. Mellor and L. E. Maley, *Nature, Lond.* **159**, 370 (1947).
7. M. Calvin and N. C. Melchior, *J. Amer. Chem. Soc.* **70**, 3270 (1948).
8. S. Ahrland, J. Chatt and N. R. Davies, *Quart. Rev.* **12**, 265 (1958).
9. J. S. Griffith and L. E. Orgel, *Quart. Rev.* **11**, 381 (1957).
10. F. G. Mann, *J. Chem. Soc.* 2681 (1926).
11. G. Schwarzenbach, B. Maissen, H. Ackermann and G. Anderegg, *Helv. Chim. Acta.* **35**, 2337 (1952).

CHAPTER V

THE EFFECT OF CO-ORDINATION ON OXIDATION POTENTIALS AND THE STABILIZATION OF VALENCY STATES

THE effect of complex formation in stabilizing certain valency states of metals is well known; familiar examples are the trivalent states of cobalt and gold. The oxidizing power of the hydrated cobaltic ion is so great that aqueous solutions of cobaltic salts, such as the sulphate or perchlorate, decompose spontaneously with the evolution of oxygen and reduction of the cobalt to the divalent state; conversely the complex cobaltocyanide ion reduces water with the formation of cobalticyanide and hydrogen. Trivalent gold provides an even more extreme example, since this valency is known only in the form of complex compounds with the square-planar co-ordination characteristic of complex compounds of d^8-ions.

The stabilization of the cobaltic ion by complex formation was explained by PAULING[1] in terms of the electronic structures of the simple and complexed ions, the stable krypton structure (effective atomic number 36) being attained in the complexes:

	$3d$					$4s$	$4p$			$5s$
Co^{3+}	↓↑	↓	↓	↓	↓	—	—	—	—	—
$[Co(CN)_6]^{3-}$	↓↑	↓↑	↓↑	↓↑ CN	↓↑ CN	↓↑ CN	↓↑ CN	↓↑ CN	↓↑ CN	
$[Co(CN)_6]^{4-}$	↓↑	↓↑	↓↑	↓↑ CN	↓↑ CN	↓↑ CN	↓↑ CN	↓↑ CN	↓↑ CN	↓

At the same time, 6:co-ordination of the Co^{2+} ion requires the promotion of one electron to a higher orbital (possibly $5s$), which can be expected to lead to powerful reducing properties. These simple explanations, however, cannot be accepted, since the hydrated Co^{3+} ion is diamagnetic and consequently similar in structure to the complexed ion (in this case, at least, the hydrated ion must be regarded as complex, just as much as the cobalticyanide ion); further, the complex cobaltocyanide has been shown to contain the $[Co(CN)_5]^{3-}$ ion in the solid state and if the Co^{2+} ion remains 5:co-ordinated in solution the necessity for promotion of an electron to an orbital beyond the krypton shell disappears[2].

When applied to the Fe^{3+}/Fe^{2+} system the theory of stabilization by the formation of a closed valency shell in the complexed condition meets with even less success; we should expect the krypton-type electronic structure of the ferrocyanide ion to stabilize the ferrous state in the complex cyanides, but the standard oxidation potentials (Table 3) show that the ferric state is, in fact, stabilized by cyanide co-ordination.

STANDARD OXIDATION POTENTIALS[3]

The criterion by which the stability of one valency state with respect to another must be measured is the standard oxidation potential of the system. The oxidation potentials of such a system in the "free" (hydrated) and complexed forms are related to one another and to the stability constants of the complexes involved; this can readily be seen if the free energy changes (ΔG°) for each successive step in the process of reduction of a complexed ion are considered:

$$M^{m+}_{aq} \quad + n\bar{e} = M^{(m-n)+}_{aq} \qquad\qquad \Delta G^\circ = -nFE^\circ_{aq} \qquad (1)$$

$$ML^{m+}_x \qquad\quad = M^{m+}_{aq} + xL \qquad\qquad\qquad + RT.\ln K_m \qquad (2)$$

$$M^{(m-n)+}_{aq} + yL = ML^{(m-n)+}_y \qquad\qquad\qquad - RT.\ln K_{m-n} \qquad (3)$$

$$\overline{ML^{m+}_x \quad + n\bar{e} = ML^{(m-n)+}_y + (x-y)L \qquad\qquad -nFE^\circ_{cx} \qquad (4)}$$

Equation (1) represents the reduction of the "free" (hydrated) ion, M^{m+} to $M^{(m-n)+}$ and E°_{aq} is the standard oxidation potential for this system; equation (4) represents the corresponding reduction of the complexed ion ML^{m+}_x for which the standard oxidation potential is E°_{cx} ; equations (2) and (3) represent the formation of the complex ions from the "free" ions and x- or y-molecules of the ligand, L, for which the stability constants are K_m and K_{m-n}, defined as:

$$K_m = \frac{[ML^{m+}_x]}{[M^{m+}_{aq}][L]^x} \qquad K_{m-n} = \frac{[ML^{(m-n)+}_y]}{[M^{(m-n)+}_{aq}][L]^y}$$

where the square brackets denote activities.

Now, since the free energy change must be the same by the direct and indirect routes, we have:

$$E^\circ_{cx} = E^\circ_{aq} - \frac{RT}{nF} \ln \frac{K_m}{K_{m-n}}$$

and consequently $E^\circ_{cx} < E^\circ_{aq}$ if $K_{m-n} < K_m$.

It is thus apparent that the stabilization of a valency state by complex formation depends upon the formation of thermodynamically more stable complexes in that valency state.   The factors which affect the stability constants of complex salts have been discussed in the previous chapter; these factors are numerous, but there are two which are dominant:

    (a)   the valency (charge) of the complexed cation; and
    (b)   the polarizability (electronegativity) of the ligand, L.

It follows that, in general, $K_{m-n} < K_m$ because of the first of these factors and that the ratio K_m/K_{m-n} is likely to increase with increasing polarizability (decreasing electronegativity) of the ligand, because of the second.

The general conclusion of this argument is that complex formation will stabilize higher valency states relative to lower and that the extent of the stabilization (i.e. $E_{aq}^\circ - E_{cx}^\circ$) will increase with increasing polarizability of

TABLE 1. EFFECT OF COMPLEX FORMATION ON THE OXIDATION
POTENTIALS OF THE Cu^+/Cu AND Ag^+/Ag COUPLES

Complex	E° (Cu^+/Cu)	E° (Ag^+/Ag)
M^+ (aqueous)	+ 0·52	+ 0·80
$M(NH_3)_2{}^+$	− 0·12	+ 0·37
MCl	+ 0·14	+ 0·22
MBr	+ 0·03	+ 0·07
MI	− 0·19	− 0·15
MSCN	− 0·27	+ 0·09
$M(CN)_2{}^-$	− 0·43	− 0·29
M_2S	− 0·93	− 0·71

the ligands.   This general conclusion applies to all systems, irrespective of the electronic structures of the particular species involved, but it must be realized that in a few cases, where the other factors affecting the stability constants of one or more of the complex ions concerned become abnormally large, discrepancies may occur.

TABLE 2. LOWERING OF OXIDATION POTENTIAL BY COMPLEX
CYANIDE FORMATION

Couple	E° (hydrated ions)	E° (complex cyanide)	ΔE°
Cu^+/Cu	+ 0·52	− 0·43	0·95
Ag^+/Ag	+ 0·80	− 0·29	1·09
Au^+/Au	+ 1·68	− 0·6	2·3
Zn^{2+}/Zn	− 0·76	− 1·32	0·56
Cd^{2+}/Cd	− 0·40	− 0·90	0·50
Hg^{2+}/Hg	+ 0·85	− 0·37	1·22
Ni^{2+}/Ni	− 0·25	− 0·91	0·66
Cr^{3+}/Cr^{2+}	− 0·86	− 1·28	0·42
Fe^{3+}/Fe^{2+}	+ 0·77	+ 0·36	0·41
Co^{3+}/Co^{2+}	+ 1·84	− 0·80	2·64
Au^{3+}/Au^+	+ 1·29	+ 0·65*	0·64
Cu^{2+}/Cu^+	+ 0·17	− 1·41†	1·58

* Thiocyanate complexes.
† Sulphides.

Unhappily, the documentation of oxidation potentials is meagre, but from the values available there is ample evidence to substantiate these general conclusions.   Experimental values for the oxidation potentials of individual systems with a number of different ligands are available in only a very few cases, of which the best documented are the Cu^+/Cu and Ag^+/Ag systems (the insoluble salts, such as the halides, being regarded as three-dimensional polymeric complexes, see Chapter III). Table 1 shows the oxidation potentials of these systems with seven different ligands arranged in order of increasing polarizability and clearly shows the successive lowering of the oxidation potential (with one value out of place in each case).

For most other systems insufficient data are available to allow adequate comparisons, but Table 2 shows the lowering effect of cyanide co-ordination on ten different systems and of thiocyanate or sulphide co-ordination on two others.

We must now consider some systems in which either special features allow the stabilization of a lower valency state by complex formation or higher valencies are stabilized which are quite unusual.

THE Fe^{3+}/Fe^{2+} SYSTEM

Whilst it is almost invariably found that complex formation stabilizes higher valency states with respect to lower, the Fe^{3+}/Fe^{2+} system provides a practically important and theoretically interesting example of the stabilization of the lower valency state. Table 3 shows some of the established oxidation potentials of this system:

TABLE 3.   OXIDATION POTENTIALS OF THE Fe^{3+}/Fe^{2+} SYSTEM

Couple	$E°$
Fe^{3+} (nitro-o-phen)$_3$/Fe^{2+} (nitro-o-phen)$_3$	$+ 1·25$
Fe^{3+} (o-phen)$_3$/Fe^{2+} (o-phen)$_3$	$+ 1·12$
Fe^{3+} (dipy)$_3$/Fe^{2+} (dipy)$_3$	$+ 1·10$
Fe^{3+} (4:7-Me$_2$-o-phen)$_3$/Fe^{2+} (4:7-Me$_2$-o-phen)$_3$	$+ 0·88$
Fe^{3+}/Fe^{2+} (aqueous)	$+ 0·77$
$Fe(CN)_6{}^{3-}$/$Fe(CN)_6{}^{4-}$	$+ 0·36$
$Fe(C_2O_4)_3{}^{3-}$/$Fe(C_2O_4)_2{}^{2-}$	$+ 0·02$
$Fe(OH)_3$/$Fe(OH)_2$	$- 0·56$

It will be observed that complexing with dipyridyl (I) or its derivatives, such as o-phenanthroline (II), raises the oxidation potential, that is stabilizes the lower valency state with respect to the upper.

This abnormal behaviour is associated with the change in magnetic properties of the ferrous ion on co-ordination (from the "outer-orbital", spin-free hydrated ion to the diamagnetic, "inner-orbital" complexed ion) with the dipyridyl derivatives and the cyanide ion. The stability of complexes of the "inner-orbital" type is invariably higher than that of "outer-orbital" complexes, particularly when associated with a closed $3d$-shell as in the ferrous 6:co-ordinated complexes; in this case, therefore, in addition to the normal lowering of oxidation potential by co-ordination, there is a tendency for an increase due to the change of electronic configuration. With the highly-polarizable cyanide ion as ligand, this second effect is insufficient to outweigh the normal co-ordination effect, so that the ferric state is stabilized in the complex cyanides, but less so than in many other systems; with the less polarizable heterocyclic bases as ligands, the lowering effect is less

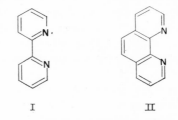

I   II

and the electronic effect overbalances it, so that the lower valency state is stabilized. It may be noted that substitution of the phenanthroline produces the normal effect, the higher valency state becoming more stable as the donor power of the nitrogen atoms increases. The phenanthrolines appear to be the group of compounds with the lowest ligand-field effect, known to enforce spin pairing in the ferrous ion.

The increased oxidation potential of the Fe^{3+}/Fe^{2+} system when co-ordinated by dipyridyl or the phenanthrolines results in a decrease of the energy required to promote the charge-transfer reaction:

$$Fe^{2+} + dipy = Fe^{3+} + dipy^-$$

which can consequently be brought about by the absorption of visible light; the resultant deep colour of the complexes, together with the convenient values of their oxidation potentials makes them valuable redox indicators for volumetric analysis.

COMPOUNDS OF DIVALENT SILVER

The oxidation potential of the Ag^{2+}/Ag^+ is so high that almost all argentic compounds decompose spontaneously due to oxidation of the anion by the argentic cation. The oxidation potential can be lowered by complex formation, but the sensitivity of most of the highly polarizable ligands to oxidation renders them unsuitable and almost all of the fairly stable argentic compounds contain the Ag^{2+} ion in co-ordination with heterocyclic bases. Dipyridyl and the phenanthrolines are amongst the most effective of the stabilizing groups:

$$Ag^{2+} \qquad + \bar{e} = Ag^+ \qquad\qquad E° = + 1·98$$
$$Ag(dipy)_2{}^{2+} + \bar{e} = Ag(dipy)_2{}^+ \qquad E° = + 0·81$$

These complex salts are orange and paramagnetic and have been shown in some cases to be isomorphous with the corresponding cupric compounds.

TRI- AND TETRA-VALENT NICKEL AND TETRAVALENT IRON

The principle of stabilization of higher valency states by ligands of low electronegativity is well illustrated by the complex compounds of Ni^{3+} and Ni^{4+}, in which the nickel atom is co-ordinated to phosphorus or arsenic atoms.

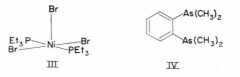

The diamagnetic, square-planar complex bis-triethylphosphine nickel bromide, $[(Et_3P)_2NiBr_2]$, can be oxidized to the corresponding trivalent nickel derivative, $[(Et_3P)_2NiBr_3]$, paramagnetic and monomeric in benzene solution, for which a square-pyramidal structure, (III), has been proposed on the basis of dipole-moment measurements[4]. The 4:co-ordinate nickel chloride derivative of the bidentate ligand o-phenylene-bis-dimethylarsine (IV), $[Ni(diarsine)_2]Cl_2$, can be similarly oxidized to the trivalent nickel derivative, which is a uni-univalent electrolyte in nitrobenzene and so regarded as a 6:co-ordinated complex, $[Ni(diarsine)_2Cl_2]Cl$; the formation of 6:co-ordinated Ni^{3+} requires the promotion of one electron beyond the krypton shell, probably to the $5s$-orbital, and consequently this compound is readily oxidized[5] to the corresponding Ni^{4+} derivative, $[Ni(diarsine)_2Cl_2]Cl_2$. The Ni^{4+} ion also occurs in some sulphur co-ordinated complexes and in the fluoride K_2NiF_6; all are diamagnetic.

	$3d$					$4s$	$4p$			$5s$
$[Ni(diarsine)_2]^{2+}$	↓↑	↓↑	↓↑	↓↑	↓↑	↓↑	↓↑	↓↑		
$[Ni(diarsine)_2Cl_2]^+$	↓↑	↓↑	↓↑	↓↑	↓↑	↓↑	↓↑	↓↑	↓↑	↓
$[Ni(diarsine)_2Cl_2]^{2+}$	↓↑	↓↑	↓↑	↓↑	↓↑	↓↑	↓↑	↓↑	↓↑	

The use of the ligand o-phenylene-bis-dimethylarsine has also made possible the stabilization of the tetravalent state of iron: with ferric chloride the doubly complex $[Fe(diarsine)_2Cl_2][FeCl_4]$ is obtained with the iron trivalent in both complex ions; this, when oxidized with nitric acid, gives the corresponding complex of tetravalent iron, $[Fe(diarsine)_2Cl_2][FeCl_4]_2$, in which the iron atom co-ordinated to four arsenic atoms is in the four valent state, as is confirmed by the paramagnetism of the compound which corresponds to the presence of two unpaired electrons on this iron atom[6].

UNIVALENT AND ZERO-VALENT NICKEL AND COBALT

Reduction of the complex nickel cyanide, $K_2[Ni(CN)_4]$, by metallic potassium in solution in liquid ammonia produces the compound $K_2Ni(CN)_3$, known as Belluci's salt. This compound is diamagnetic and must thus be polymerized since the monomeric compound would contain an odd number of electrons. X-ray analysis has established the bridged structure (V), and since infra-red analysis reveals only the normal $C\equiv N$ stretching frequencies of the cyanide ion it is concluded that the bridging groups must be linked by three-centre bonds[7]. Further reduction of the nickel cyanide complex under the same conditions gives the Ni° complex, $K_4[Ni(CN)_4]$. Corresponding compounds of palladium and cobalt in the zero-valent state are obtained in the same way.

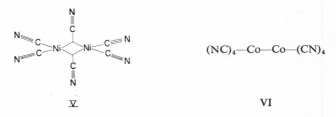

$$(NC)_4\text{—Co—Co—}(CN)_4$$

V   VI

The nickel and palladium compounds are diamagnetic and presumably have tetrahedral anions. The $[Ni(CN)_4]^{4-}$ ion would be isoelectronic with the nickel carbonyl molecule, $Ni(CO)_4$, the unusual stabilization of the low Ni° valency by cyanide co-ordination being attributed to the possibility of double bonding between the nickel and carbon atoms as in the carbonyl:

$$Ni{\leftarrow}C\equiv N{-} \quad \longleftrightarrow \quad Ni{\rightleftarrows}C{=}N{<}$$

The cobalt compound is very feebly paramagnetic and so probably dimeric; by analogy with the carbonyl, $Co_2(CO)_8$, an ion with Co—Co bonds is postulated (VI) [8].

Univalent cobalt is known in the form of the dipyridyl complexes, reduction of the trivalent complex $[Co(dipy)_3]\,(ClO_4)_3$ with sodium borohydride giving the univalent complex $[Co(dipy)_3]\,(ClO_4)$ [9].

REFERENCES

1. L. PAULING, *Nature of the Chemical Bond.* Cornell University Press, New York (1942).
2. A. W. ADAMSON, *J. Amer. Chem. Soc.* **73**, 5710 (1951).
3. W. M. LATIMER, *The Oxidation States of the Elements and their Potentials in Aqueous Solution.* Prentice-Hall, New York (1938).
4. K. A. JENSEN and B. NYGAARD, *Acta Chem. Scand.* **3**, 474 (1949).
5. R. S. NYHOLM, *J. Chem. Soc.* 2061 (1950); 2602 (1951).
6. R. S. NYHOLM and R. V. PARISH, *Chem. & Ind.* 470 (1956).
7. M. F. A. EL SAYED and R. K. SHELINE, *J. Amer. Chem. Soc.* **78**, 702 (1956).
8. W. HIEBER and C. BARTENSTEIN, *Z. anorg. Chem.* **276**, 12 (1954).
9. A. A. VLČEK, *Nature, Lond.* **180**, 753 (1957).

CHAPTER VI

CARBONYLS AND π-COMPLEXES

THE discovery of nickel and iron carbonyls by Mond in 1890 and his use of the former in the nickel-refining process known by his name opened up a new field of chemistry, characterized by the formation of compounds by metals in the zero-valent state. The direct action of carbon monoxide under pressure on metals in a finely-divided state gives carbonyls only with iron, cobalt, nickel, molybdenum, rhenium and ruthenium; carbonyls of other transition metals are obtained by the action of carbon monoxide on their compounds in organic solvents during their reaction with Grignard reagents or by the reaction between carbon monoxide and the *cyclo*pentadienyls at elevated temperatures.

In all known carbonyls the metal atom acquires the electronic structure of the next inert gas. Thus only the metals of even atomic number in groups VI–VIII form monomeric carbonyls, the stereochemistry of which is that expected for compounds with co-ordination numbers of six, five and four: the $M(CO)_6$ carbonyls of the group VI elements form octahedral molecules; those of iron, ruthenium and osmium have trigonal bipyramidal $M(CO)_5$ molecules and nickel carbonyl, $Ni(CO)_4$, is tetrahedral; corresponding carbonyls of palladium and platinum are not known.

	3d					4s	4p		
$Cr(CO)_6$	↓↑	↓↑	↓↑	↓↑ CO	↓↑ CO	↓↑ CO	↓↑ CO	↓↑ CO	↓↑ CO
$Fe(CO)_5$	↓↑	↓↑	↓↑	↓↑	↓↑ CO	↓↑ CO	↓↑ CO	↓↑ CO	↓↑ CO
$Ni(CO)_4$	↓↑	↓↑	↓↑	↓↑	↓↑	↓↑ CO	↓↑ CO	↓↑ CO	↓↑ CO

Electron diffraction studies of nickel carbonyl also showed that the Ni—C—O groups were linear, with unexpectedly short Ni—C bonds, the measured bond length of 1·82 Å being 0·37 Å shorter than that calculated for a Ni—C single bond; the C—O distance of 1·15 Å is intermediate between that of the C—O double and triple bonds. These results are interpreted as indicating considerable contribution to the structure from the double-bonded form (II), which is produced by "back co-ordination" of the non-bonding $3d$-electrons on the nickel atom to the carbon monoxide molecules [1, 1a].

$$ \text{Ni} \leftarrow \text{C} \equiv \text{O} \text{—} \quad \longleftrightarrow \quad \text{Ni} \rightleftarrows \text{C} = \text{O}\langle $$
$$ \text{(I)} \qquad\qquad\qquad\qquad \text{(II)} $$

The simplest carbonyls of the intervening elements of odd atomic number are dimeric, manganese and rhenium forming $Mn_2(CO)_{10}$ and $Re_2(CO)_{10}$ and cobalt $Co_2(CO)_8$ in accordance with the principle of completion of the inert-gas structure of the metal atom; the molecular complexities of the carbonyls of rhodium and iridium of the type $[M(CO)_4]_n$ are not known, but are probably similar. These dimeric carbonyls of manganese, rhenium

	$3d$					$4s$	$4p$		
					CO	CO	CO	CO	CO
$Mn_2(CO)_{10}$	↓↑	↓↑	↓↑	↑	↓↑	↓↑	↓↑	↓↑	↓↑
	↓↑	↓↑	↓↑	↓	↓↑	↓↑	↓↑	↓↑	↓↑
					CO	CO	CO	CO	CO
					CO	CO	CO	CO	
$Co_2(CO)_8$	↓↑	↓↑	↓↑	↓↑	↑	↓↑	↓↑	↓↑	↓↑
	↓↑	↓↑	↓↑	↓↑	↓	↓↑	↓↑	↓↑	↓↑
					CO	CO	CO	CO	

and cobalt* have been shown to have the two halves of the molecule linked by direct metal–metal bonds (III), (IV)[2].

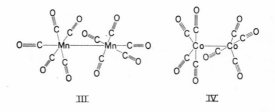

III   IV

$Ni(CO)_4$ (b.p. 43°C), $Fe(CO)_5$ (b.p. 103°C), $Ru(CO)_5$, $Os(CO)_5$ and $Co_2(CO)_8$ are liquids, the last three decomposing below 100°C to give polymeric solid carbonyls; the other carbonyls are all solids, those of the group VI metals subliming at temperatures of 100–200°C without decomposition, though all carbonyls are eventually decomposed to the metals and carbon monoxide by heat, the nickel compound particularly readily; all are

* A more recent high-resolution infra-red study suggests, however, that a bridged structure may be more probable for $Co_2(CO)_8$ [2a].

immiscible with water but more or less soluble in organic solvents; the readily-volatile carbonyls, such as the nickel and iron compounds, are very poisonous.

On exposure to light or heat iron carbonyl loses carbon monoxide with the formation of a yellow, solid, dimeric carbonyl, $Fe_2(CO)_9$, which disproportionates above 60°C giving $Fe(CO)_5$ and a dark green solid carbonyl $Fe_3(CO)_{12}$, the molecular weight of which was determined by the depression of freezing point of the pentacarbonyl.

$$6Fe(CO)_5 - 3CO \xrightarrow{\text{light}} 3Fe_2(CO)_9 \xrightarrow[60°C.]{} Fe_3(CO)_{12} + 3Fe(CO)_5$$

All these carbonyls are diamagnetic, so that the iron atom probably has the inert-gas structure of krypton in each case. The structure of the enneacarbonyl, $Fe_2(CO)_9$, has been determined by X-ray analysis[3]: the iron atoms are linked by three covalent "ketonic" $\rangle C=O$ bridges, and as the Fe—Fe

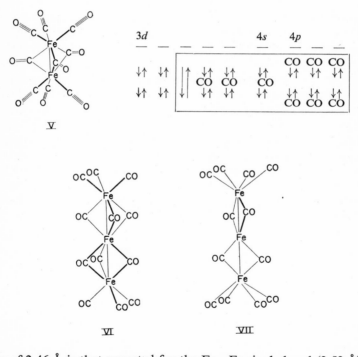

V

VI   VII

distance of 2·46 Å is that expected for the Fe—Fe single bond (2·52 Å), it is concluded that this is also present, thus bringing the electronic structure of each iron atom up to that of the next inert gas and accounting for the diamagnetism (V). The structure of the trimeric tetracarbonyl, $Fe_3(CO)_{12}$, is not known, even the exact positions of the iron atoms being uncertain; but these appear to be collinear and since the infra-red absorption shows the presence of both ketonic, bridging, $>C=O$ groups and terminal carbonyl—$C\equiv O$ groups, structures have been proposed akin to that of the enneacarbonyl (VI), (VII).

Ruthenium and osmium pentacarbonyls also decompose on gentle heating to give the corresponding carbonyls, $Ru_2(CO)_9$ and $Os_2(CO)_9$, but the existence of more highly-polymerized compounds is doubtful. On heating to 50°C cobalt carbonyl, $Co_2(CO)_8$, loses carbon monoxide giving a black, highly-reactive, tetrameric tricarbonyl, $Co_4(CO)_{12}$, the structure of which is unknown.

CARBONYL HYDRIDES AND CARBONYL HALIDES

Although insoluble in water, iron and cobalt carbonyls dissolve in alkalis, and on acidification give the carbonyl hydrides, $H_2Fe(CO)_4$ and $HCo(CO)_4$, as volatile liquids decomposing a little above room temperatures. Investigation of their structures by electron diffraction shows that the four —CO groups are arranged tetrahedrally about the metal atom as in nickel carbonyl, one of the Co—C bond lengths in the cobalt compound being longer (1·83 Å) than the other three (1·75 Å); as the infra-red absorption shows no bands characteristic of the —OH group[4], it is concluded that the hydrogen atom is linked to the other three —CO groups by multi-centre bonds involving the non-bonding electrons on the oxygen atoms or, perhaps, the bonding electrons of the —$C\equiv O$ group (VIII). As might be expected, the hydrogen atoms in these carbonyl hydrides are acidic, the anions $[Fe(CO)_4]^{2-}$ and $[Co(CO)_4]^-$ being isoelectronic with nickel carbonyl. The salts, particularly those of heavy metals, are readily obtained by the action of salts of these metals on solutions of the carbonyls in alkali or ammonia, and in a few cases direct syntheses of these salts have been achieved, for example that of the zinc salt, $Zn[Co(CO)_4]_2$, by heating cobalt bromide and finely divided zinc with carbon monoxide under pressure.

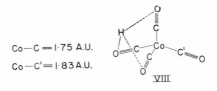

Co—C $= 1\cdot75$ A.U.

Co—C$' = 1\cdot83$ A.U.

VIII

Carbonyl anions have now been shown to be present in several of the ammine–carbonyls formed by the action of amines on carbonyls[5]. Thus, the compounds formerly represented as $Fe_4(CO)_{11}(en)_3$, $Fe_3(CO)_8(en)_3$ and $Fe_2(CO)_4(en)_3$, obtained by the action of ethylenediamine (en) on iron tetra-carbonyl at successively higher temperatures, are now thought to be salts of the tris-ethylenediamine ferrous ion with the carbonyl anions $[Fe_3(CO)_{11}]^{2-}$, $[Fe_2(CO)_8]^{2-}$ and $[Fe(CO)_4]^{2-}$; in the same way, the action of ammonia on mercuric cobalt carbonyl, $Hg[Co(CO)_4]_2$, gives $Co_3(CO)_8(NH_3)_6$, now recognized as the salt $[Co(NH_3)_6] [Co(CO)_4]_2$.

The carbonyl halides, $Fe(CO)_2X_2$, $Fe(CO)_4X_2$ and $Fe(CO)_5X_2$, formed by the action of halogens on iron carbonyl or the carbonyl salts, such as $Hg[Fe(CO)_4]$, however, cannot be of this type as they are soluble and monomeric in organic solvents. The structures of those with two and five carbonyl groups are unknown, but the tetracarbonyl halides are presumably octahedral molecules. It is significant that the iodides are the most stable of these compounds, as we should expect if the non-bonding electrons on the iron atom are to be available for back co-ordination to the carbonyl groups.

ISONITRILES AND PHOSPHORUS COMPLEXES[5a]

The —CO group in the carbonyls can be replaced by a number of other groups, which are able to allow back co-ordination of the d-electrons of the metal atom. Among these are the *iso*nitriles, RNC; thus, iron pentacarbonyl reacts with *iso*nitriles giving compounds of the type $Fe(CO)_3(CNR)_2$ and chromium carbonyl gives $Cr(CO)_3(CNR)_3$. Hexa*iso*nitriles of chromium, molybdenum and tungsten[6] are obtained by reaction between aryl*iso*-cyanides and chromous acetate or the covalent halides of the heavier metals (IX).

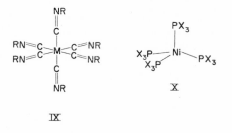

IX

In the same way, trivalent phosphorus compounds (but not the corresponding nitrogen compounds, as the nitrogen atom cannot accept back co-ordinated electrons) react with nickel carbonyl to give tetra-tri-substituted-phosphine nickels (X); compounds of this type are known with a wide range of phosphorus compounds and one of them, $Ni(PCl_2Me)_4$, has been obtained by the direct action of boiling dichloromethylphosphine in nickel turnings[7].

NITROSYLS

The principle of maintenance of the effective atomic number of the metal atom in carbonyl-like compounds is well illustrated by the reactions of iron enneacarbonyl and cobalt carbonyl with nitric oxide, which forms the mixed carbonyl–nitrosyls $Fe(CO)_2(NO)_2$ and $Co(CO)_3(NO)*$. These substances have simple tetrahedral molecules with linear M—C—O and M—N—O groups, and since the replacement of a —CO group by —NO involves an increase of one electron in the system, are both isoelectronic with nickel carbonyl. As in nickel carbonyl, the M—C and M—N bonds are shortened, indicating some degree of double-bonding by back co-ordination from the metal atoms.

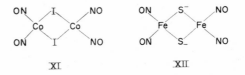

XI   XII

Ferrous and cobaltous halides, particularly the iodides, also react with nitric oxide, giving compounds of the type $M(NO)_2X$. The iron compounds are very reactive, but those of cobalt, which melt at 100–130°C, are stable to air and react only slowly with water; their structure is unknown, but the dimeric halogen-bridged formula (XI) has been proposed as preserving the effective atomic number of 36 on the cobalt atoms. The related structure (XII) has been proposed for the anion $[Fe_2(NO)_4S_2]^{2-}$, found in the diamagnetic Roussin's red salts, which are obtained when nitric oxide reacts with ferrous salts in the presence of a sulphide, and the Roussin's black salts first formed are treated with alkali.

NITROPRUSSIDES AND COMPLEX ACETYLIDES

In the carbonyls and analogous compounds so far described the metal atoms are characterized by a formal valency state zero. The —CO, —NO and related groups can, however, also be introduced into co-ordination compounds of the transition metals in their usual valency states. For example, carbon monoxide reacts with a hot ferrocyanide solution to give the anion, $[Fe(CN)_5(CO)]^{3-}$, of carbonylferrocyanic acid, which can be isolated from the acidified solution as a pale yellow crystalline hydrate, $H_3[Fe(CN)_5(CO)].H_2O$. Another example is the red-brown "nitroprusside", $K_2[Fe(CN)_5(NO)]$, obtained when potassium ferrocyanide is heated with 5 N nitric acid, and familiar for its colour reactions with sulphides (purple) and reactive methylene groups (red in alkaline solution, turning green on acidification).

From their formulae the "nitroprussides" appear to be nitrosoferricyanides with trivalent iron, but their diamagnetism shows that they must be derivatives of ferrous iron (krypton structure in octahedral complexes) with

---

* A third member of this series, $Mn(CO)(NO)_3$, has now been obtained[7a].

the nitric oxide co-ordinated as NO⁺, the odd electron of the nitric oxide molecule being transferred to the iron atom:

	3d					4s	4p		

$[Fe^{III}(CN)_6]^{3-}$ ↓↑ ↓↑ ↓ ↓↑ ↓↑ ↓↑ ↓↑ ↓↑ ↓↑ paramagnetic
　　　　　　　CN CN CN　CN CN CN

$[Fe^{III}(CN)_5(NO)]^{2-}$ ↓↑ ↓↑ ↓ ↓↑ ↓↑ ↓↑ ↓↑ ↓↑ ↓↑ paramagnetic
　　　　　　　N CN CN CN CN CN
　　　　　　•O

$[Fe^{II}(CN)_5(\overset{+}{NO})]^{2-}$ ↓↑ ↓↑ ↓↑ ↓↑ ↓↑ ↓↑ ↓↑ ↓↑ ↓↑ diamagnetic
　　　　　　　N CN CN CN CN CN
　　　　　　+O

$[Fe^{II}(CN)_5(CO)]^{3-}$ ↓↑ ↓↑ ↓↑ ↓↑ ↓↑ ↓↑ ↓↑ ↓↑ ↓↑ diamagnetic
　　　　　　　CO CN CN CN CN CN

The groups CN⁻, CO and NO⁺ are isoelectronic and the complex ions $[Fe(CN)_6]^{4-}$, $[Fe(CN)_5(CO)]^{3-}$, and $[Fe(CN)_5(\overset{+}{NO})]^{2-}$ differ only in the nuclear charges (atomic numbers) of the atoms in the sixth ligand. Also isoelectronic with these ions is the acetylide ion, C_2^{2-}, and within the past 10 years a considerable range of complex acetylides has been obtained.

The simple acetylides are all very unstable, but replacement of one of the hydrogen atoms of acetylene by an alkyl, or better, aryl group considerably increases the stability. In liquid ammonia solution, for example, ferrous thiocyanate and potassium acetylides give the hexa-acetylido complexes, $K_4[Fe(C_2R)_6]$, and nickel hexammine thiocyanate gives tetra-acetylido complexes, $K_2[Ni(C_2R)_4]$, analogous to the normal complex cyanide of divalent nickel [8, 8a].

XIII

While the monosubstituted acetylenes have an acidic hydrogen atom and consequently form donor anions of the type RC_2^-, as in the above examples, disubstituted acetylenes cannot do this. Nevertheless some complexes are known in which disubstituted acetylenes act as ligands, for example the platinum compounds $[(Ph_3P)_2Pt(C_2R_2)]$, obtained by reduction of *cis*-$[(Ph_3P)_2PtCl_2]$ in the presence of the acetylenes [9]. These complexes, in which the platinum appears to be zero-valent are most stable when the acetylene is substituted by aryl groups; the acetylene molecules apparently act as bidentate ligands in agreement with the observation that the infra-red absorption shows the triple bond to have been opened (XIII).

OLEFIN COMPLEXES

Chloroplatinites react with olefins in two stages, a chloride ion being replaced by a molecule of the olefin at each stage. Thus, with ethylene:

$$[PtCl_4]^{2-} \rightarrow [PtCl_3(C_2H_4)]^- \rightarrow [PtCl_2(C_2H_4)_2]^\circ$$

Formation of the mono-olefin salt, known as Zeise's salt, is shown by the colour change of the chloroplatinite solution from red to yellow; extraction of this yellow aqueous solution with ether gives the neutral compound $[PtCl_2(C_2H_4)]_2$, containing one less ethylene group attached to each platinum atom and shown by depression of freezing point in benzene to be dimeric and by dipole moment methods to have the *trans*-planar bridged structure (XIV).

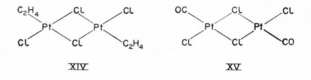

Other olefins can be used instead of ethylene, but the complexes are less stable, being decomposed in some cases even by carbon monoxide, with the formation of the carbonyl chlorides, $[PtCl_3CO]^-$ and $[PtCl_2CO]_2$ (XV). All of these compounds are decomposed by cyanide with the formation of platinocyanide, $[Pt(CN)_4]^{2-}$, and quantitative liberation of olefin or carbon monoxide.

The ethylene complexes were originally thought to contain bonds of this type:

$$Pt \leftarrow CH_2 \leftarrow CH_2$$

but infra-red absorption indicates that the symmetry of the olefin molecules is retained and X-ray analysis shows that the olefin is bound to the platinum by "sideways" co-ordination, the fourth co-ordination position of the platinum being taken by the centre of the C=C double bond (XVI). CHATT[10] has suggested that the bonding involves co-ordination of the π-electrons of the double bond to the platinum atom and that the strength of the bond is reinforced by "back co-ordination" of non-bonding electrons on the platinum atom (possibly in *dp*-hybrid orbitals) to the antibonding π-orbital of the olefin molecule (XVII).

Olefin complexes of this type are also known in which a doubly unsaturated molecule behaves as a bidentate ligand, filling two co-ordination positions on the metal atom and being bound by co-ordination of the π-electrons of the

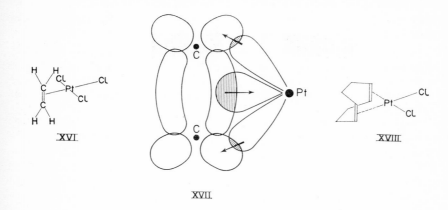

XVI XVII XVIII

double bond in each position; the *cyclo*octa-1:5-diene complexes (XVIII) being particularly stable[11].

THE *CYCLOPENTADIENYLS*[12, 12a]

In 1951 unsuccessful attempts to oxidize *cyclo*pentadienyl magnesium bromide (XXI) to di*cyclo*pentadienyl (XXII) with ferric chloride in solution in organic solvents resulted in the isolation of an iron derivative, $FeC_{10}H_{10}$, an orange solid, m.p. 173°C, soluble in organic solvents, at first formulated as a normal organometallic compound (XXIII). About the same time this compound was also obtained by the direct reaction between *cyclo*-pentadiene and a reduced iron catalyst at 350–400°C[13, 14].

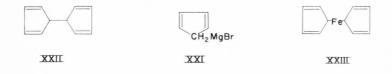

XXII XXI XXIII

The development of synthetic methods has now led to the preparation of similar compounds of many other metals, mostly of the form $MC_{10}H_{10}$, isomorphous with the iron compound and melting within a few degrees of the same temperature. All these compounds clearly have similar molecular structures and the observation that all have zero dipole moment and show only one type of C—H absorption in the infra-red is interpreted as indicating a "sandwich" type of structure (XXIV), subsequently confirmed by electron diffraction and X-ray analysis of the iron compound, which has, in the solid state, ten equal Fe—C distances of 2·04 Å and ten equal C—C distances of 1·40 Å. This C—C distance corresponds to that in benzene, and if these compounds are regarded as formed by co-ordination of two *cyclo*pentadienyl anions ($C_5H_5^-$) to a divalent cation, this can be readily understood, as the "aromatic" nature of the $C_5H_5^-$ ion is familiar to the organic chemist.

The iron compound was thus regarded as the first member of a new series of aromatic compounds and named "ferrocene". Its aromatic character is shown by a number of reactions in which it undergoes ring substitution, under conditions similar to those commonly leading to substitution in benzene[15].

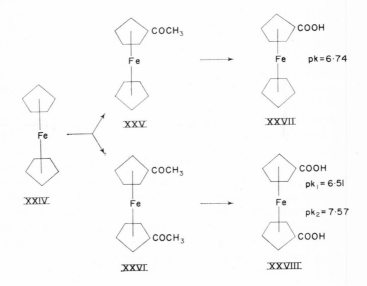

Thus, Friedel–Crafts acylation is brought about by the action of acetyl chloride and aluminium chloride, mono- and di-acetyl derivatives being obtained (XXV, XXVI), which can be reduced to ethyl derivatives or oxidized to carboxylic acids (XXVII, XXVIII); these acids are comparable in strength to benzoic acid (pk, under similar conditions, $= 6·62$) and the very small difference between the first and second dissociation constants of the dicarboxylic acid shows that the carboxyl groups are in separate rings.

Although sulphonation can be carried out in acetic anhydride solution, giving mono- and di-sulphonic acids, more vigorous substituting agents, such as nitric acid or halogens, oxidize the ferrocene to blue salts of the "ferricinium" cation, $Fe(C_5H_5)_2^+$, in which the iron is trivalent; the positive charge on this cation then makes substitution impossible. The ferricinium salts, easily obtained in this way, can be reduced back to ferrocene by, for example, stannous chloride. A value of $+ 0.30$ V is quoted for the oxidation potential of the $Fe(C_5H_5)_2^+/Fe(C_5H_5)_2$ couple, comparable to that for the ferricyanide/ferrocyanide couple[16].

The direct action of *cyclo*pentadiene on metals is only an effective method of preparing *cyclo*pentadienyls in the case of iron, and since the formation of ferrocene from the Grignard reagent of *cyclo*pentadiene and ferric chloride clearly depends upon the homogeneity of the reaction, general methods of preparation have been based on the use of co-ordination compounds of the metals, soluble in organic solvents.

Benzene- or ether-soluble complexes of several metals have been found to react with the Grignard reagent, *cyclo*pentadienyl magnesium bromide, to give *cyclo*pentadienyls. Nickel acetylacetonate[17], for example, gives nickel *cyclo*pentadienyl, $Ni(C_5H_5)_2$, as dark green crystals, m.p. 172°C, and vanadium tetrachloride gives the vanadium compound, $V(C_5H_5)_2$, m.p. 168°C, dark violet[18]. Under the same conditions cobaltic acetylacetonate[19] gives the cobaltic cation, $Co(C_5H_5)_2^+$, isoelectronic with ferrocene and stable in aqueous solution from which the anions of some very strong acids precipitate insoluble salts, such as the tetraphenylborate, $[Co(C_5H_5)_2]^+[BPh_4]^-$.

The cobalticinium ion, $Co(C_5H_5)_2^+$, resists all attempts at reduction to cobaltocene, $Co(C_5H_5)_2$. This compound has, however, been made by the reaction between tetrammine cobaltous thiocyanate and lithium *cyclo*pentadienyl in liquid ammonia: the salt $[Co(NH_3)_6]^{2+}2C_5H_5^-$ first obtained decomposes on heating *in vacuo*, giving a sublimate of dark violet cobaltocene, very easily oxidized to the cobalticinium ion (compare other complexes of divalent cobalt, such as $Co(CN)_6^{4-}$). The bright red chromium compound, $Cr(C_5H_5)_2$, can be similarly obtained via the salt $[Cr(NH_3)_6]$ $(C_5H_5)_3$, and reaction of ferric chloride with indenyl lithium in ether gives bis-indenyl iron (XXIX), a purple solid, m.p. 185°C.

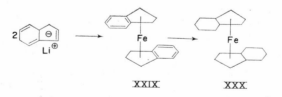

XXIX   XXX

The aromatic character of the *cyclo*pentadienyl ring is decreased by fusion of the benzene ring (compare naphthalene) and oxidation of the indenyl compound cannot be accomplished without destruction of the molecule; hydrogenation, however, preferentially reduces the benzene ring and the orange bis-tetrahydroindenyl iron (XXX) obtained can readily be oxidized to the blue cation $Fe(C_9H_{11})_2^+$[20].

G

By the action of the more reactive sodium *cyclo*pentadienyl on manganese bromide in tetrahydrofuran as solvent, the manganese compound, $Mn(C_5H_5)_2$ has been obtained. This compound exists in two different modifications: at ordinary temperatures it is a brown solid with a magnetic moment of about 1β (β = Bohr's magneton); as the temperature rises the magnetic moment changes gradually, reaching a maximum of about $5\cdot8 \beta$ above 160°C, the

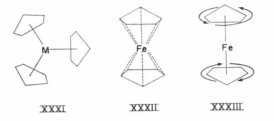

XXXI   XXXII   XXXIII

change being accompanied by a loss of the brown colour; the white form produced melts sharply at 173°C and can be preserved by rapid cooling. This peculiar change in properties is analogous to a change from low-spin to high-spin electronic configuration[21]. This method of preparation, using the sodium *cyclo*pentadienyl in tetrahydrofuran, has also given a series of *cyclo*pentadienyls of the lanthanide elements[22] of the form $M(C_5H_5)_3$, probably with the structure (XXXI), the three metal–ring links being coplanar at angles of 120°.

ELECTRONIC STRUCTURE OF THE *CYCLO*PENTADIENYLS[23]

The iron atom has eight electrons in its valency shell, which can accommodate eighteen; since the $C_5H_5\cdot$ radical has five electrons in excess of those involved in the interatomic σ-bonds, the earlier descriptions of the ferrocene molecule envisaged the co-ordination of all these electrons to complete the inert-gas structure of the iron atom, the bonding being, in effect, by five one-electron Fe—C bonds to each ring (XXXII). The failure to isolate isomeric forms of the disubstituted ferrocenes, such as (XXVI) and (XXVIII), and other evidence for the free rotation of the rings about the line of centres has led, however, to the rejection of this structure in favour of one in which the *cyclo*pentadienyl rings are bound to the metal atom by π-bonds (XXXIII).

The *cyclo*pentadienyls can then be regarded either as π-bound complexes of the $C_5H_5\cdot$ radicals with the neutral metal atom or as complexes of the anions, $C_5H_5^-$, with the divalent metal cation. The aromatic character of the ring in these compounds suggests that the latter approach is preferable.

The $C_5H_5^-$ anion has an "aromatic sextet" of non-σ-bonding electrons, the lowest energy molecular orbitals of which are as follows:

(1) A Σ-orbital, spheroidal in shape and extending over the whole molecule, analogous to an atomic *s*-orbital (XXXIV).

(2) Two Π-orbitals, broadly dumbbell-shaped, oriented at right angles to one another, and analogous to atomic p-orbitals (XXXV, XXXVI):

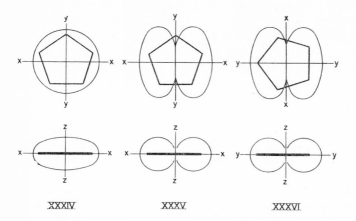

XXXIV   XXXV   XXXVI

Plans and elevations of the molecular orbitals of the
*cyclo*pentadienyl anion

In the $C_5H_5^-$ ion all of these lowest orbitals are doubly occupied; the two Π-orbitals, which are of equal energy (i.e. degenerate), provide the bonding electrons.

The iron atom is oriented with the z-axis in the line of centres of the two rings and the electrostatic repulsion of the non-bonding electrons in the *cyclo*pentadienyl Σ-orbital raises the energy of the atomic d_{z^2}-orbital so far, that hybridization with the $4s$-orbital can occur, producing two new, more compact, hybrid ds-orbitals, one of which is of lower energy than the original d_{z^2}-orbital, and one of higher. The atomic orbitals, in order of increasing energy, thus become:

high ds-hybrid	——		$(4s, 3d)\ \sigma_+$
$3d_{xz},\ 3d_{yz}$	——	——	$3d\pi$
low ds-hybrid	——		$(4s, 3d)\sigma_-$
$3d_{xy},\ 3d_{x^2-y^2}$	——	——	$3d\delta$

Energy levels of atomic orbitals in complexes
of ferrocene type

Bond formation occurs mainly by co-ordination of the electrons in the Π-orbitals of the *cyclo*pentadienyl anions to the $3d\pi$ orbitals of the metal atom, which have suitable symmetry (XXXVII). In ferrocene, therefore, the six original electrons of the ferrous ion are paired in the three lowest atomic orbitals (two $3d\delta$ and σ_-) and four more electrons are donated from the *cyclo*pentadienyl anion Π-orbitals to the metallic $3d\pi$-orbitals. The molecule thus has all of its electrons paired and is diamagnetic. Oxidation to the ferricinium ion removes one electron (probably from the σ_--orbital) giving a paramagnetic ion with one uncompensated spin ($\mu = 2.26\ \beta$). The chromium

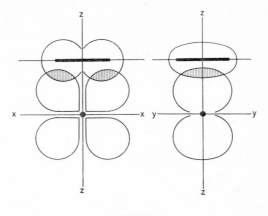

XXXVII

Front and side views of overlap between the Π_x-orbital of the cyclopentadienyl anion and the $3d_{xz}$-orbital of the metal ion

and vanadium compounds are also paramagnetic with two and three unpaired electrons, respectively, as expected, and the magnetic properties of the other cyclopentadienyls can be interpreted in a similar manner.

THE "CHROMIUM PHENYLS" AND RELATED COMPOUNDS[12a]

The "sandwich" structure of the cyclopentadienyls is the result of co-ordination to a metal ion of the π-electrons of an aromatic system and similar compounds can be expected with other aromatic systems, in particular with benzene itself, of which the chromium compound, $Cr(C_6H_6)_2$, would be isoelectronic with ferrocene, and so likely to be the most stable compound of this type.

Chromium phenyl halides of the form $Cr(Ph)_nX$ were obtained by Hein as early as 1919[24] by the action of phenyl magnesium bromide on anhydrous chromic chloride in organic solvents. Electrolytic reduction of these salts gave the diamagnetic "chromium phenyls", $CrPh_3$ and $CrPh_4$, since shown by reduction with lithium aluminium deuteride to contain, respectively, one and two diphenyl groups[25] and so to be formulated $Cr(C_6H_6)(C_{12}H_{10})$ and $Cr(C_{12}H_{10})_2$. The simplest member of the series, dibenzene chromium, $Cr(C_6H_6)_2$, has been prepared from the reaction of chromium chloride with aluminium chloride, aluminium and benzene at high temperature: hydrolysis of the reaction mixture gives the salt $Cr(C_6H_6)_2{}^+Cl^-$, which is reduced by hydrosulphite to black, diamagnetic dibenzene chromium, melting at 284°C, decomposing a little above its melting point into chromium and benzene, and shown by X-ray analysis to have a "sandwich" structure (XXXVIII).

In this method of preparation benzene can be replaced by other aromatic hydrocarbons, giving substituted compounds, such as bis-mesitylene chromium (XXXIX) from mesitylene and bis-diphenyl chromium (XL)

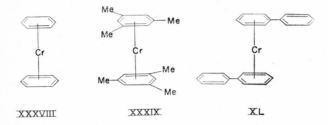

XXXVIII   XXXIX   XL

from diphenyl; this last compound can be oxidized to a cation, $Cr(C_{12}H_{10})_2{}^+$, the iodide of which is identical with Hein's "tetraphenyl chromium iodide". From rhenium pentachloride the same method of preparation gave salts of the corresponding bis-aryl rhenium cations, $Re(Ar)_2{}^+$, which could not be reduced; corresponding salts of the divalent cations $Fe(Ar)_2{}^{2+}$ and $Ru(Ar)_2{}^{2+}$ have also been obtained; these ions are analogous to the cobalticinium ion in the *cyclo*pentadienyl series[26].

Since ferrocene, dibenzene chromium and the cations obtained with rhenium, iron and ruthenium are all isoelectronic, neutral "sandwich" molecules may be expected for the metals of group VII in combination with one aromatic ring and one *cyclo*pentadienyl anion, and a red, diamagnetic manganese compound of this type has been obtained by the action of phenyl magnesium bromide on methyl*cyclo*pentadienyl manganese chloride[27].

Theoretically any aromatic system should be able to form compounds with the "sandwich" structure, but in heterocyclic systems this type of π:co-ordination is usually prevented by the preference of the ligand for normal co-ordination via the hetero-atom; pyridine and other heterocyclic bases, for instance, always co-ordinate via the nitrogen atom. However, a few "sandwich" compounds are known with thiophenes as π-donors (the electro-negativities of carbon and sulphur are not widely different, particularly when that of the sulphur is reduced by conjugation of the non-bonding pairs with the unsaturated system), and by blocking the donor properties of the nitrogen atom by quaternary salt formation, it has been possible to form "sandwich" compounds with pyridine[28].

CYCLOPENTADIENYL CARBONYLS

Reaction of the *cyclo*pentadienyls with carbon monoxide under pressure or of the carbonyls with *cyclo*pentadiene at elevated temperatures yields mixed carbonyl*cyclo*pentadienyls. Thus, by the action of carbon monoxide the *cyclo*pentadienyls of vanadium, manganese and cobalt give the mixed compounds $V(C_5H_5)(CO)_4$, $Mn(C_5H_5)(CO)_3$ and $Co(C_5H_5)(CO)_2$. These compounds are all monomeric and diamagnetic, suggesting analogy with the carbonyls of the alternate elements chromium, iron and nickel; and if the *cyclo*pentadiene ion, $C_5H_5^-$, is considered as donating *all* its π-electrons the metals in these mixed compounds have, as in the carbonyls, the electronic structure of the next inert gas[29]. The expected formation of dimeric *cyclo*pentadienylcarbonyls by the intervening elements is illustrated by the compounds $[Cr(C_5H_5)(CO)_3]_2$, $[Mo(C_5H_5)(CO)_3]_2$, $[W(C_5H_5)(CO)_3]_2$ and $[Fe(C_5H_5)(CO)_3]_2$ (XLI). The molybdenum compound has been shown to have direct Mo—Mo bonds linking the two halves of the dimer (XLII)[30].

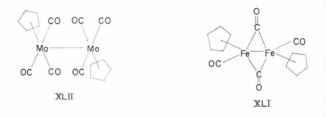

A number of related compounds is also known in which some of the —CO groups are replaced by the isoelectronic —NO⁺ or CN⁻ or by PX_3 molecules, for example the nickel compound $(C_5H_5)Ni(NO)$, isoelectronic with the unknown $Cu(C_5H_5)(CO)$, which would be the terminal member of the series of *cyclo*pentadienylcarbonyls formed by vanadium, manganese and cobalt.

ANHYDROUS METAL NITRATES

These interesting compounds have been obtained only in the last 2 or 3 years and their structures are not yet completely established, but it appears that they may form an addition to the range of "sandwich" compounds wholly inorganic in nature.

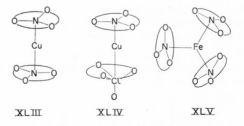

Metallic copper is attacked rapidly by nitrogen tetroxide in ethyl acetate solution, the compound $Cu(NO_3)_2.N_2O_4$ crystallizing from the solution. On heating at 100°C this compound loses its solvent of crystallization, leaving blue, anhydrous cupric nitrate, which sublimes below 200°C. The vapour is monomeric and electron diffraction studies are consistent with the "sandwich" structure (XLIII)*. A similar nitrate perchlorate (probably XLIV) and an anhydrous ferric nitrate (XLV) have also been made[31].

REFERENCES

1. L. O. BROCKWAY and J. S. ANDERSON, *Trans. Faraday Soc.* **33**, 1233 (1937).
1a. L. E. ORGEL, *Recent Developments in the Theory of Metal to Ligand Bonds.* Chemical Society, Special Publication (1959).
2. L. F. DAHL, E. ISHISHI and R. E. RUNDLE, *J. Chem. Phys.* **26**, 1750 (1957).
2a. F. A. COTTON and R. R. MONCHAMP, *J. Chem. Soc.* 1882 (1960).
3. H. M. POWELL and R. V. G. EWENS, *J. Chem. Soc.* 286 (1939).
4. W. F. EDGELL, C. MAGEE and G. GALLUP, *J. Amer. Chem. Soc.* **78**, 4185 (1956).
5. W. HIEBER, R. WERNER, J. SEDLMEIER and J. G. FLOSS, *Chem. Ber.* **90**, 278, 1116, 1617 (1957).
5a. L. MALATESTA, *Progr. Inorg. Chem.* **1**, 283, Interscience, New York (1959).
6. L. MALATESTA, A. SACCO, S. GHIELMI and M. GABAGLIO, *Gazz. Chim. Ital.* **82**, 516, 548 (1952).
7. L. D. QUIN, *J. Amer. Chem. Soc.* **79**, 3681 (1957).
7a. C. G. BARRACLOUGH and J. LEWIS, *Proc. Chem. Soc.* 81 (1960).
8. R. NAST and R. URBAN, *Z. Naturf.* **8b**, 381 (1953); *Z. anorg. Chem.* **287**, 17 (1956); **289**, 244 (1957).
8a. R. NAST, *Complex Acetylides of Transition Metals.* Chemical Society, Special Publication (1959).
9. J. CHATT, G. A. ROW and A. A. WILLIAMS, *Proc. Chem. Soc.* 208 (1957).
10. J. CHATT and L. A. DUNCANSON, *J. Chem. Soc.* 2939 (1953).
11. J. CHATT, L. M. VALLARINO and L. M. VENANZI, *J. Chem. Soc.* 2496, 3413, 4735 (1957).
12. P. L. PAUSON, *Quart. Rev.* **9**, 391 (1955).
12a. G. WILKINSON and F. A. COTTON, *Progr. Inorg. Chem.* **1**, 1, Interscience, New York (1959).
13. P. L. PAUSON and T. J. KEALY, *Nature, Lond.* **168**, 1039 (1951).
14. S. A. MILLER, J. A. TEBBOTH and J. F. TREMAINE, *J. Chem. Soc.* 632 (1952).
15. R. B. WOODWARD, M. ROSENBLUM and M. C. WHITING, *J. Amer. Chem. Soc.* **74**, 3458 (1952).
16. G. WILKINSON and J. A. PAGE, *J. Amer. Chem. Soc.* **74**, 6149 (1952).
17. G. WILKINSON, P. L. PAUSON and F. A. COTTON, *J. Amer. Chem. Soc.* **76**, 1970 (1954).
18. J. M. BIRMINGHAM, A. K. FISCHER and G. WILKINSON, *Natürwissenschaften* **42**, 96 (1955).
19. G. WILKINSON, *J. Amer. Chem. Soc.* **74**, 6148 (1952).
20. E. O. FISCHER and D. SEUS, *Z. Naturf.* **8b**, 694 (1953); **9b**, 386 (1954).
21. G. WILKINSON, F. A. COTTON and J. M. BIRMINGHAM, *J. Inorg. Nucl. Chem.* **2**, 95 (1956).
22. G. WILKINSON and J. M. BIRMINGHAM, *J. Amer. Chem. Soc.* **76**, 6210 (1954).
23. D. P. CRAIG, A. MACCOLL, R. S. NYHOLM, L. E. ORGEL and L. E. SUTTON, *J. Chem. Soc.* 332 (1954).
24. F. HEIN, *Ber. dtsch. chem. Ges.* **52**, 195 (1919).
25. F. A. COTTON, *Chem. Rev.* **55**, 551 (1955).

---

* In the solid state, however, anhydrous cupric nitrate consists of polymeric chains of $[Cu(NO_3)]_n^{n+}$ interspersed by nitrate ions, each co-ordinated to three Cu^{2+} ions in different chains[32] and there is no apparent relationship between this structure and the remarkable properties of the molecular compound.

26. E. O. Fischer and R. Böttcher, *Z. anorg. Chem.* **291**, 305 (1957).
27. T. H. Coffield, V. Sandell and R. D. Closson, *J. Amer. Chem. Soc.* **79**, 5826 (1957).
28. B. Moore and G. Wilkinson, *Proc. Chem. Soc.* 61 (1959).
29. E. O. Fischer, R. Jira and W. Hafner, *Z. Naturf.* **9b**, 503, 618 (1954); **10b**, 355 (1955).
30. F. C. Wilson and D. P. Shoemaker, *J. Chem. Phys.* **27**, 809 (1957).
31. C. C. Addison, B. J. Hathaway and N. Logan, *Proc. Chem. Soc.* **51** (1958).
32. S. C. Wallwork, *Proc. Chem. Soc.* 311 (1959).

CHAPTER VII

SOME PRACTICAL APPLICATIONS

THOUGH many of the most recent advances in co-ordination chemistry have yet to find industrial uses, complex salts have a long history of practical significance. Of course, in many of the earliest applications, such as the dissolution of gold in aqua regia or the refinement of platinum by precipitation of potassium chloroplatinate, it was more or less of an accident that complex compounds were involved, and no deliberate attempt was made to utilize their special properties.

Amongst these, largely accidental, uses of co-ordination compounds some of the most important involve the complex fluorides of the lighter metals. Thus, in the production of metallic aluminium by the electrolytic reduction of alumina, the complex fluoride, Na_3AlF_6, which occurs naturally as the rather rare mineral cryolite, is used as a flux to lower the working temperature. Complex fluorides of beryllium, scandium, titanium, columbium and tantalum are also important metallurgically, largely because they are almost the only readily available compounds of these metals which resist hydrolysis. The differing resistance to hydrolysis of the complex fluoride ions of columbium, CbF_7^{2-}, and tantalum, TaF_7^{2-}, is the basis of the classical separation of these two very similar metals, the former being hydrolysed to the $CbOF_5^{2-}$ ion under conditions which do not affect the tantalum complex.

Where solubilities are low analytical applications may be possible and some common complex anions give very insoluble precipitates with metallic cations. Potassium ferrocyanide, for example, is used as a reagent for zinc, silver, copper, molybdenum, uranium and other metals because of the highly-insoluble and, often, deeply-coloured precipitates which are produced; the most familiar of these is the deep blue ferric salt, used as a pigment under the name "prussian blue". Satisfactory blue pigments and dyestuffs are peculiarly difficult to obtain and for many years prussian blue and the silicate pigment ultramarine were almost the only ones available. The discovery of copper phthalocyanin (monastral blue) has, however, now provided another blue pigment of outstanding properties and slight variations of shade are being obtained by substitution in the organic part of the molecule.

The characteristic colour of some co-ordination compounds has led to their use as colour tests in analysis. The well-known colour change of cobaltous solutions from pink to blue, for example, is due to the formation of complexes such as $CoCl_3^-$ and $CoCl_4^{2-}$, and more sensitive versions of this test are based on the formation of analogous complexes of higher stability, such as the thiocyanate complex obtained on addition of ammonium thiocyanate to cobaltous solutions, the blue colour in this case being extracted by organic solvents such as amyl alcohol. Other familiar examples are the red ferric thiocyanate complex and the blue cuprammine complex.

Numerous attempts have been made to find some application for the many metallic ammines, largely without success. Recently, however, it has been found that strong hydrochloric acid solutions of divalent cobalt can be quantitatively oxidized by oxygen and ammonia in the presence of activated charcoal, and highly-purified cobalt can be made by recrystallization of the hexammine cobaltic chloride thus obtained. Ores containing cobalt, nickel and copper are also being extracted by selective leaching with ammonia solution under pressure, separation of the metals depending on the resistance of the various ammines so formed to reduction by hydrogen under pressure.

One of the peculiarities associated with co-ordination chemistry is the possibility of obtaining neutral, covalent, molecular, compounds of metals which, in their simple compounds, form ionic salts. These neutral compounds usually have low solubilities in water and are often readily volatile and may consequently be used in the separation of the metals concerned from contaminants. Familiar examples are the precipitation of divalent palladium as the diammine chloride, $Pd(NH_3)_2Cl_2$, the separation of the isotopes of uranium by the gaseous diffusion of the hexafluoride, and the refining of osmium and nickel by volatilization of the tetroxide and carbonyl, respectively.

INNER COMPLEXES

$Ni(CO)_4$, UF_6, and $Pd(NH_2)_2Cl_2$ are examples of neutral compounds in which the metal atoms are attached to simple ligands. Such compounds are

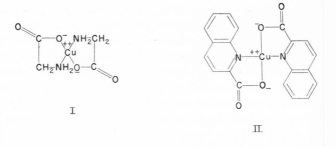

I

II

comparatively few and often difficult to make, but an immense range of neutral compounds is accessible by the co-ordination of singly-charged bidentate ligands. These anions form neutral complexes with cations having co-ordination numbers double their valency, such as Pd^{2+}, Cu^{2+}, Zn^{2+}, Al^{3+},

Cr^{3+}, Co^{3+} and Th^{4+} and many others. These neutral, chelate complexes are known as "inner" complexes.

Any organic chemist is familiar with the inner complexes formed by copper and the amino acids. On mixing hot solutions of cupric sulphate and sodium glycinate a deep blue-violet colour is produced which deposits deep blue needles of cupric glycinate on cooling. The copper salt is sparingly soluble in cold water, almost a non-electrolyte and resistant to hydrolysis, though decomposed by acids. As early as 1904 Ley suggested the cyclic formula (I) for this compound and applied conductivity experiments to show the decreased stability of the six- and seven-membered rings formed by the anions of β-alanine and γ-aminobutyric acid. Whilst cupric glycinate and the α- and β-alaninates are appreciably soluble in water, the higher homologues become highly insoluble and have been used for the quantitative precipitation of copper, particularly good results being obtained with quinaldinic acid, the heterocyclic nitrogen and carboxylate anion acting as donors to form five-membered chelate rings (II).

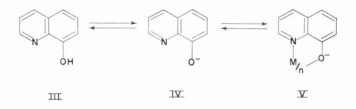

III.   IV.   V.

Another example of the participation of a heterocyclic nitrogen atom in the chelate ring is provided by 8-hydroxyquinoline (III), "oxine", the anion of which (IV) co-ordinates with numerous metallic cations to give inner complexes (V). Since in acid solutions the metal and hydrogen ions are in direct competition for the oxinate anion and in alkaline solutions the oxinate and hydroxyl ions are in competition for the metal cation, there is a limited pH range of stability of the complex, characteristic for each metal, and dependent on the complex stability constants and the metal–hydroxyl ion association constants. These pH ranges, some values of which are given in Table 1, differ sufficiently for useful quantitative separations to be possible.

TABLE 1. pH RANGES OF COMPLETE PRECIPITATION OF OXINATES

Cation	Cu^{2+}	Fe^{3+}	Al^{3+}	Zn^{2+}	Th^{4+}	Ti^{4+}	Mn^{2+}	Mg^{2+}	Ca^{2+}
pH range	> 2·7	2·8–11·2	4·2–9·8	> 4·4	4·4–8·8	4·8–8·6	5·9–10	> 8·2	> 9·2

In practice oxine is most often used for the estimation of aluminium, zinc and magnesium (since alternative methods are available for transition metals), aluminium and zinc being precipitated at pH 5, when magnesium remains in solution to be precipitated later from an ammoniacal chloride solution. In the presence of tartrate zinc may be precipitated while aluminium remains in solution and the extension of this type of control has made oxine one of the most versatile reagents, particularly as there are often alternative methods of completing the analysis: by weighing the precipitated complex after drying at 110°C, by igniting to the metal oxide and weighing this, or by solution in acid and estimation of the oxine in solution iodimetrically.

An important group of phenolic chelating agents is that in which the phenolic group has as neighbour a nitrosyl group. These compounds form particularly stable cobalt complexes, α-nitroso-β-naphthol (VI) being commonly used as a reagent for divalent cobalt, which forms the insoluble, red inner complex even in acetic acid solution. The inner complex (VII) can be solubilized by sulphonation of the naphthalene rings and the deep red colour produced in solution by combination of divalent cobalt with nitroso-R-salt (VIII) is a very sensitive test for this metal.

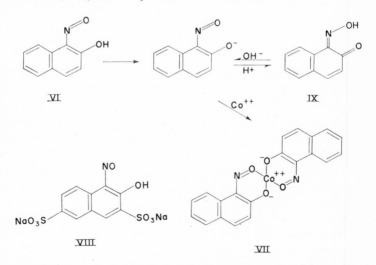

The nitrosophenols are tautomeric with the quinone monoximes (IX) and a number of other oximes with donor groups appropriately placed relative to the oxime group are capable of forming inner complexes. Salicylaldoxime (X), for example, forms an insoluble cupric complex (XI) even in acidic solutions and a clean separation of copper from nickel is provided by the solubility of the nickel complex under these conditions, though it is quantitatively precipitated from ammoniacal solution. It will be noticed that the oxime group co-ordinates through the nitrogen atom. Oximes always co-ordinate in this way, as is shown by the behaviour of the stereoisomeric benzoinoximes. The α-oxime ("cupron") is a useful reagent for copper, giving a precipitate of the cupric inner complex in ammoniacal solutions; this isomer has the anti-configuration (XII), but the syn-isomer (β-benzoinoxime) has the hydroxyl group so placed as to obstruct chelation and forms no cupric complex (XIII).

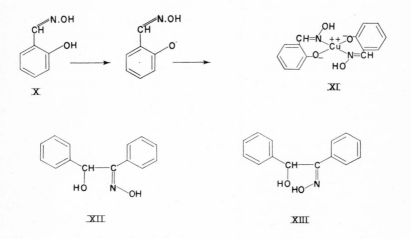

The difference in behaviour of the three isomers (XIV–XVI) of dimethylglyoxime provided the earliest evidence for N:co-ordination in the familiar nickel complex, formed in ammoniacal solution. Only the antiform (XVI) gives the pink-red nickel complex. The N:co-ordination has been confirmed by X-ray analysis, which also reveals some peculiarities of this compound,

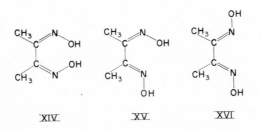

resulting in its specificity for nickel under controlled conditions: one of the hydroxyl groups in each dimethylglyoxime molecule becomes ionized and hydrogen bond formation results in reinforcement of the chelation and planarity (XVII). In addition to this the molecules are so packed in the crystal that successive molecules lie above one another and the Ni—Ni distances are short enough to allow some orbital interaction in the long chain of nickel atoms so formed; it is this system, resulting from the d^8-structure of the Ni^{2+} ion, which is responsible for the unusual colour of the complex.

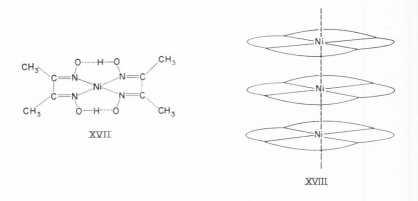

In the reagent "cupferron" nitrosyl and hydroxyl groups are attached to the same aromatic amino nitrogen atom (XIX) and co-ordination occurs through the oxygen atoms (XX). First developed as a reagent for copper, this reagent is particularly valuable as a precipitant for iron, titanium or zirconium from strongly-acid solutions, in which conditions aluminium, chromium, zinc, magnesium and most other metals do not react.

The analogy often made between nitrosyl and carbonyl groups leads us to expect chelation by juxtaposed phenolic and ketonic groups. The most familiar examples are provided by the α-hydroxyanthraquinones which form "lakes" with many metal cations, particularly those forming amphoteric or very weakly-basic hydroxides. Thus, in neutral or weakly-alkaline solution, alizarin (XXI) gives blue- to red-coloured precipitates (lakes) with Al^{3+}, Sn^{4+}, Ti^{4+}, Be^{2+}, etc. As with the cobalt nitrosonaphthols, these coloured complexes can be solubilized by sulphonation and "alizarin red S" (XXII) is useful as a reagent, particularly for aluminium, zirconium and scandium, which give colours in neutral or slightly acid solutions. Decolorization of the zirconium lake by fluorides (which preferentially form the ZrF_6^{2-} complex ion) may be used as a quantitative method for fluoride ions.

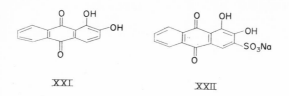

XXI   XXII

Carbonyl and acidic hydroxyl groups are also juxtaposed in the enolate ions (XXIV) of β-diketones, such as acetyl acetone (XXIII), which form highly-stable inner complexes with many metals (XXV). The copper complex forms steely blue needles, soluble in organic solvents but not in water, and so resistant to thermal decomposition that it can be sublimed unchanged

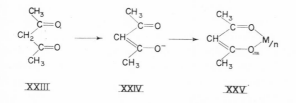

XXIII   XXIV   XXV

about 400°C. Many tetravalent ions exhibit their maximum covalency of eight in acetylacetonates such as $Zr(acac)_4$, $Ce(acac)_4$ and $Th(acac)_4$. The stabilities of these β-diketone complexes vary considerably with the nature of the ketones, benzoylacetone and dibenzoylmethane, for example, forming more stable complexes than acetylacetone, while those formed by trifluoracetylacetone and ethyl acetoacetate are of lower stability.

SOLVENT EXTRACTION

The electrical neutrality of inner complexes, which is responsible for their low solubility in water, frequently leads to an appreciable solubility in organic media; consequently, in the presence of ligands which can form inner complexes, many metals can be extracted into a water-immiscible organic phase, a process of value in both analytical and industrial separations.

The β-diketones, for example, have been applied to numerous separations. The best results have been obtained using the more acidic compounds such as trifluoracetylacetone (XXVI) or a α-thenoyltrifluoracetone (TTA, XXVII), by means of which a reasonably effective separation of zirconium and hafnium has been achieved, a process of great importance in removing hafnium (which has a high neutron capture cross-section) from zirconium for use in atomic reactors. Beryllium and scandium, also valuable nuclear engineering metals, have also been refined by solvent extraction in the presence of TTA.

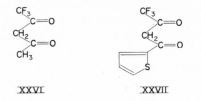

XXVI   XXVII

Fundamentally, solvent extraction from aqueous solutions depends upon the competition of hydrogen ions and metal cations for the ligand anion (A^-):

$$OH_2 + HA \rightleftharpoons OH_3^+ + A^-$$
$$M^{n+} + nA^- \rightleftharpoons MA_n$$

The distribution of the metal between the phases thus depends on the acidity constant of the ligand acid and the stability constant of the inner complex and is sensitive to changes in pH. It is for this reason that the most satisfactory results are obtained with the more acidic ligands. It must be realized, however, that few extraction equilibria conform at all exactly to the simple distribution pattern derived from the above equations as complicating factors are nearly always present, such as solvation and polymerization effects, and even in some instances the slowness with which equilibrium is reached.

$$S=C \begin{cases} NH-NH-C_6H_5 \\ N=N-C_6H_5 \end{cases}$$

XXVIII

Many organic inner-complex forming ligands have been used in solvent extraction processes, but only a very few have proved of outstanding value. One of these is dithizone (diphenylthiocarbazone, XXVIII). A chloroform solution of this compound is capable of extracting many metals from aqueous solution almost quantitatively, and in some cases gives solutions of characteristic colour. It is particularly useful for the detection and estimation of lead, which gives a red chloroform solution, suitable for colorimetry. Zinc, which is simultaneously extracted into the chloroform layer, can be effectively separated by back-extraction with aqueous potassium thiocyanate. Iron, when present in large quantities, is usually removed by formation of the complex with cupferron (XX), which can be extracted with ether. Cupferron has also been used in the refinement of a number of metals by the solvent extraction method, including protoactinium, and oxine (III) has been made the basis of a number of separation processes, particularly of the metals of group IIIB.

These metals, however, are particularly well separated by ether extraction of solutions of their chlorides in strong hydrochloric acid: gallium is almost quantitatively extracted into the ether layer as $HGaCl_4$, while indium and aluminium remain in the aqueous layer, indium probably because of the lower stability of the $InCl_4^-$ complex ion and aluminium because the acid $HAlCl_4$ is too highly ionized; trivalent thallium accompanies gallium into the ether phase but is, of course, readily removed by reduction to the univalent state.

In the six-valent state molybdenum, likewise, is almost quantitatively extracted by ether from 6 N hydrochloric acid, leaving chromium and tungsten behind, but here more convenient methods of separation are available. Ether extraction from strong hydrochloric acid solution does, however, provide a convenient means of separating gold from all its neighbours, the gold passing into the organic phase as $HAuCl_4$; the extraction of gold is even more effective from hydrobromic acid solution.

Gold can also be extracted almost quantitatively by ether from 8 N nitric acid, dissolving in the organic phase presumably as the complex acid $HAu(NO_3)_4$, salts of which are known. So few metals form stable nitrate complexes that extraction from strong nitric acid solutions by organic oxygenated solvents such as ether, ketones or phosphates provides nearly specific methods for the refinement of these metals. Only tetravalent cerium, which forms stable 6:co-ordinated complex nitrates, is extracted as effectively as gold, presumably as $H_2Ce(NO_3)_6$; some 35 per cent of thorium is extracted under the same conditions and about 65 per cent of six-valent uranium (as uranyl nitrate) and this method has been used for the refinement of uranium for atomic energy purposes. Extraction of these metals occurs only from very strong nitric acid solutions, possibly because of the suppression of ionization of the complex-nitrate acids; it is not affected by highly-ionized nitrates, such as KNO_3 or $Ba(NO_3)_2$, but is facilitated by the presence of some other nitrates, notably those of ferric iron, zinc and lithium, suggesting that non-ionized or slightly-ionized double nitrates may be formed, such as $Li_2Ce(NO_3)_6$, but our knowledge of the detailed physical chemistry of these systems is still slight.

SEQUESTRATION

Considerable use has been made of the ability of co-ordinating groups to suppress the normal reactions of metal cations. In the presence of complex-forming ligands, an equilibrium:

$$M^{n+} + xL \rightleftharpoons ML_x^{n+}$$

H

is set up and reduces the concentration of M^{n+} ions in solution, thus preventing reactions, such as precipitation processes, which depend on the concentration of free cations. The extent to which reactions are inhibited depends on the stability constants of the complexes formed and the solubility product of the precipitate.

Familiar examples of this "sequestering" power from routine analytical procedures include the precipitation of bismuth as the hydroxide, $Bi(OH)_3$, by ammonia in the presence of copper and cadmium, which are held in solution as the ammines $[Cu(NH_3)_4]^{2+}$ and $[Cd(NH_3)_4]^{2+}$, and the separation of copper from cadmium by the action of hydrogen sulphide on solutions of the complex cyanides, $[Cu(CN)_4]^{3-}$ and $[Cd(CN)_4]^{2-}$, only the cadmium complex giving the insoluble sulphide under these conditions. The interference of organic acids in qualitative analysis is also due to the comparatively high stabilities of the complexes which are formed with ions such as Al^{3+} and Fe^{3+}, and advantage is taken of the complexing power of tartaric acid in several analytical procedures: in mineral analysis, for example, iron may be separated from aluminium, titanium and zirconium by precipitation with hydrogen sulphide from ammoniacal tartrate solution, when the iron is reduced to the divalent state and precipitates as ferrous sulphide, while the presence of the tartrate prevents the precipitation of the other metals as hydroxides. Yet another example of the application of organic acids is the separation of calcium and magnesium in the presence of an excess of oxalate, calcium oxalate remaining undissolved, whilst the magnesium goes into solution as the oxalato-complex, $[Mg(C_2O_4)_2]^{2-}$.

The term "sequestration", however, is usually used to refer to the suppression of those precipitation reactions of calcium and magnesium which are responsible for the "hardening" of water. The precipitation of soaps as their calcium or magnesium salts by hard water can be prevented by the complexing of the metal cations; the formation of scale, consequent on the boiling of temporarily hard water, and dependent on the reactions:

$$2HCO_3^- = H_2O + CO_2 + CO_3^{2-}$$
$$M^{2+} + CO_3^{2-} = MCO_3$$

can be similarly prevented, but, of course, the accumulation of solids in boilers, due to the evaporation of water, cannot be controlled in this way.

In practice, two main types of complexing agent have been used for the sequestration of calcium and magnesium ions in water: phosphates and polydentate amino acids.

The addition of certain phosphates to hard water produces precipitates of calcium and magnesium salts which redissolve on addition of excess of the phosphate solution, probably due to complex formation; in the presence of the excess of phosphate soaps give no precipitate, so that the water has been effectively softened. The effectiveness of the phosphates as sequestering agents depends upon the nature of the phosphate anion: orthophosphates have very little effect and indeed, sodium orthophosphate will not redissolve the precipitate of calcium orthophosphate produced. The sequestering power of the polyphosphates is much greater, the most satisfactory results being obtained with the polyphosphate glasses in the composition range $Na_2O:P_2O_5 = 1 : 1\cdot1–1\cdot3$, where the molecular weight of the anion corresponds to a chain length of from four to eight units, sometimes referred to as "hexametaphosphate". The precise nature of the phosphate complexes formed is not known.

Polydentate amino acids, such as nitrilotriacetic acid and ethylenediamine-tetra-acetic acid (EDTA) also form highly-stable complexes with Mg^{2+} and Ca^{2+} ions and are widely used in water softening, the latter being known commercially as "sequestrene" or "complexone". The extraordinary stability of the EDTA complexes arises from the possibility of forming from the same ligand up to five five-membered chelate ring systems (XXIX) and is high enough to prevent the precipitation of calcium or magnesium by all ordinary reagents and even of barium by sulphate.

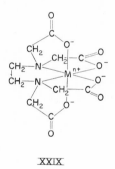

XXIX

EDTA is also used as a titrant for the volumetric estimation of calcium, magnesium and other metals, indicators being based on the principle of competitive complex formation by complex-forming dyes. The indicator solochrome black (XXX), for instance, gives a blue solution in water at pH $6\cdot3–11\cdot5$ but forms a wine-red complex with calcium or magnesium ions. On addition of EDTA to the wine-red solution, the metal ions are removed by preferential complex formation and when the last trace of metal ion has been removed the blue colour of the indicator reappears. With murexide (XXXI) as indicator, magnesium forms no coloured complex but calcium forms a pink complex, the colour of which gives way to the blue colour of the indicator anion when the calcium is preferentially complexed on addition of EDTA. Other metals can be titrated by adding more than enough EDTA to complex them and back titrating the excess with magnesium or calcium, as in the titrimetric finish to the estimation of lead or barium as sulphate.

Closely related to the sequestration processes are those which involve adsorption or desorption of ions on zeolites or ion-exchange resins. Such processes have long been in use for the removal of calcium and magnesium from hard water, the zeolite or resin acting as an anchored complexing framework, which co-ordinates the more highly-charged Ca^{2+} and Mg^{2+} ions in preference to sodium ions. The most spectacular results have been achieved, however, in the separation of the lanthanide elements. We should expect

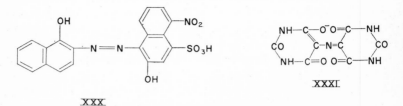

XXX   XXXI

that those lanthanide ions which are of smaller radius would be more effectively adsorbed on ion-exchange resins, but in practice it is not possible to obtain a satisfactory separation by the simple process of adsorption followed by elution with water or dilute acid. Very effective separation has been obtained, however, by the competitive method: the metals are first adsorbed on the resin and then eluted with a solution of a complexing anion, the order of appearance in the eluent depending on the stabilities of the complexes formed. In the earliest experiments of this type citrate was used as eluent, but even better results have been obtained using nitrilotriacetate, EDTA or other amino acid or hydroxyamino acid complexing agents.

BIBLIOGRAPHY

GENERAL THEORETICAL AND REFERENCE BOOKS

E. CARTMEL and G. W. A. FOWLES, *Valency and Molecular Structure*. Butterworth, London (1956).

W. M. LATIMER, *Oxidation States of the Elements and their Potentials in Aqueous Solution* (2nd Ed.). Prentice–Hall, New York (1952).

L. PAULING, *The Nature of the Chemical Bond* (2nd Ed.). Cornell University Press, New York (1940).

N. V. SIDGWICK, *The Chemical Elements and Their Compounds*. Oxford University Press (1950).

A. F. WELLS, *Structural Inorganic Chemistry* (2nd Ed.). Oxford University Press (1950).

BOOKS ON VARIOUS ASPECTS OF CO-ORDINATION CHEMISTRY

J. C. BAILAR (Editor), *Chemistry of the Co-ordination Compounds*. Reinhold, New York (1956).

F. BASOLO and R. G. PEARSON, *Mechanisms of Inorganic Reactions—A Study of Metal Complexes in Solution*. John Wiley, New York (1958).

Chemical Society, Special Publications: *Kinetics and Mechanisms of Inorganic Reactions in Solution* (1957). *Stability Constants* (1958). *Proceedings of the International Conference on Co-ordination Chemistry, London* (1959).

G. E. COATES, *Organo-metallic Compounds*. Methuen, London (1956).

H. J. EMELEUS and J. S. ANDERSON, *Modern Aspects of Inorganic Chemistry* (2nd Ed.). Routledge and Kegan Paul, London (1952).

W. C. JOHNSON (Editor), *Organic Reagents for Metals*. Hopkin and Williams, London (1955).

J. A. KITCHENER, *Ion-exchange Resins*. Methuen, London (1957).

A. E. MARTELL and M. CALVIN, *Chemistry of the Metal Chelate Compounds*. Prentice–Hall, New York (1952).

G. SCHWARZENBACH, *Complexometric Titrations*. Interscience, New York (1957).

P. W. SELWOOD, *Magnetochemistry*. Interscience, New York (1943).

REVIEW ARTICLES

A. R. BURKIN, Stabilities of complex compounds. *Quart. Rev.* **5**, 1 (1951).

J. W. CABLE and R. K. SHELINE, Bond hybridization and structure in the metal carbonyls. *Chem. Rev.* **56**, 1 (1956).

J. CHATT, S. AHRLAND and N. R. DAVIES, Relative affinities of ligand atoms for acceptor molecules and ions. *Quart. Rev.* **12**, 265 (1958).

F. A. COTTON, Alkyls and aryls of the transition metals. *Chem. Rev.* **55**, 551 (1955).

J. S. GRIFFITH and L. E. ORGEL, Ligand-field theory. *Quart. Rev.* **11**, 381 (1957).

H. M. N. H. IRVING, The application of solvent extraction to inorganic analysis. *Quart. Rev.* **5**, 200 (1951).

L. MALATESTA, Isocyanide complexes of the metals, *Progr. Inorg. Chem.* **1**, 283, Interscience, New York (1959).

F. S. MARTIN and R. J. W. HOLT, Liquid–liquid extraction in inorganic chemistry, *Quart. Rev.* **13**, 327 (1959).

101

R. S. NYHOLM, Magnetism and inorganic chemistry. *Quart. Rev.* **7**, 377 (1953).

R. S. NYHOLM and R. J. GILLESPIE, Inorganic stereochemistry. *Quart. Rev.* **11**, 339 (1957).

R. S. NYHOLM and A. MACCOLL, The stereochemistry of complex compounds. *Progr. in Stereochem.* **1**, 322 (1954).

L. E. ORGEL, Charge-transfer spectra and some related phenomena. *Quart. Rev.* **8**, 422 (1954).

P. L. PAUSON, Ferrocene and related compounds. *Quart. Rev.* **9**, 391 (1955).

D. D. PERRIN, Oxidation-reduction potentials of complex ions, *Rev. Pure and Appl. Chem.* **9**, 257 (1959).

H. M. POWELL, Unusual types of co-ordination compound. *J. Inorg. Nucl. Chem.* **8**, 546 (1958).

G. SARTORI, The polarography of metal complexes. *J. Inorg. Nucl. Chem.* **8**, 196 (1958).

L. E. SUTTON, The theory of bonding in metal complexes. *J. Inorg. Nucl. Chem.* **8**, 23 (1958).

H. TAUBE, Mechanisms of redox reactions of simple chemistry. *Advanc. in Inorg. Chem. Radiochem.* **1** (1959).

J. R. VAN WAZER and C. F. CALLIS, Metal complexing by phosphates. *Chem. Rev.* **58**, 1011 (1958).

G. WILKINSON and F. A. COTTON, Cyclopentadienyls and arene metal compounds, *Progr. Inorg. Chem.* **1**, 1, Interscience, New York (1959).

AUTHOR INDEX

Reference numbers are shown in parentheses after the page numbers.
Initials are omitted where literature is not cited.

SUBJECT INDEX